Is Fred Dead?

A Manual on Sexuality for Men with Spinal Cord Injuries

by

Robert W. Baer, Psy.D.

DORRANCE PUBLISHING CO., INC.
PITTSBURGH, PENNSYLVANIA 15222

i

ISBN # 0-8059-6444-4
Printed in the United States of America

First Printing

For information or to order additional books, please write:
Dorrance Publishing Co., Inc.
701 Smithfield Street
Third Floor
Pittsburgh, Pennsylvania 15222
U.S.A.
1-800-788-7654
Or visit our web site and on-line catalog at www.dorrancepublishing.com

Table of Contents

About the Author

Robert W. Baer, Psy.D., Dr. Baer was born and raised in central Pennsylvania. In July of 1982 at the age of seventeen, he suffered a C4-C5 spinal cord injury as the result of a diving accident. He received his rehabilitation at Shriners Hospital in Philadelphia, Pennsylvania, and later at the Milton H. Hershey Medical and Rehabilitation Center located in Hershey, Pennsylvania.

After graduating from Mechanicsburg Senior High School in 1984, he attended Edinboro University of Pennsylvania where he received his bachelor's degree in Psychology in 1987 and his master's degree in Clinical Psychology in 1989. Dr. Baer graduated with his doctoral degree (PsyD) in clinical psychology from The Forest Institute of Professional Psychology in 2003. Dr. Baer currently lives in Dickinson, ND with his wife, Susan, and there German Shepherd, Gretchen.

Acknowledgments

This manual has been in the making for a very long time. A project of this magnitude can only become reality with the help of others. Over the years many professionals and friends with spinal cord injuries have provided me with their input, suggestions, and shared personal experiences regarding their sexuality issues. I would personally like to thank every one of them.

In developing and writing this manual there is a special group of individuals whom I would like to thank for their assistance and guidance; Tristi Benitez, Jeff Bryce, Ginelle Frank, Dan Hammack, Dr. Pam Edwards, Dr. Karen Lee, Don Morgan, Dr. Frances Parks, and Kent Quiggle. The assistance of these individuals helped to move this manual from a vision in my mind to a reality in form.

I would like to give special thanks and acknowledgement to three very special individuals for all their help and assistance with making this manual become a reality. Richard Brzezinski, a good friend of the family, has spent many long hours editing this manual from cover to cover. Barbara Nelson, for her many hours spent scanning and rescanning each picture and guiding me with her knowledge and experience to bring this manual together. Finally, my friend Richard Polson. Richard worked long and hard hours to bring to life the illustrations and images I envisioned. His artistic talent and abilities that brought this manual to life go well beyond my expectations.

I would also like to give a special thanks to Susan Colvin, President of California Exotics, and her staff. Ms. Colvin supported this project by allowing me to review and show her company's products. She also shares my belief that individuals with disabilities have the right to sexual expression and the right to pursue a satisfying sex life.

Finally, I am most grateful to my wife, Susan, for her wisdom, inspiration, love, and support toward me and my work. Susan has spent many long hours editing, screening, and offering suggestions. She has been my ongoing source of motivation and strength throughout this process.

Introduction

Currently, there are over 200,000 individuals living in the United States with spinal cord injuries (SCIs). Each year there are approximately 10,000 new reported cases of individuals who sustain a SCI. Spinal cord injuries primarily affect young adults between the ages of 16 and 30, although the number of spinal cord injuries occurring to older adults has been increasing steadily in recent years. As the "baby boomers" begin to move into late adulthood and join the growing U.S. senior population, their desire to stay active combined with the physical effects of aging places them at a higher risk of being injured. Spinal cord injuries are often the result of motor vehicle accidents, acts of violence, falls, and sporting accidents. Eighty-two percent of those individuals who sustain a spinal cord injury are males. This means that for every one woman who has a spinal cord injury there are four men who are injured (National Spinal Cord Statistical Center, 1999).

The process of adjusting to a spinal cord injury can seem overwhelming. Individuals are faced with many uncertainties about themselves, their relationships with others, and the impact their injury will have on their future. The adjustment process takes time, self-determination, and support from others. As they enter a rehabilitation program, the main focus of their treatment is to help them regain their independence through the process of physical strengthening and learning daily living skills. The goal of treatment is to get them back into the community as quickly as possible. Because of cuts in hospital budgets, down sizing of staff, and limits imposed by managed care, hospital stays and programs offered during the rehabilitation process have been greatly reduced. According to the National Spinal Cord Statistic Center (1999), since 1974 the length of stay for an individual in an acute care unit of a hospital immediately following an injury has decreased from 26 days to 14 days in 1997. The same is true for post-acute rehabilitation settings where the stay has dropped from 115 days to 46 days. Thus, those issues that were not learned or discussed during the course of the rehabilitation process become the patients' responsibility after they are discharged from the rehabilitation center.

One area often neglected during the rehabilitation process is educating the individual about issues relating to sexuality following a spinal cord injury. This manual focuses on issues that are often a major concern for men who have spinal cord injuries.

The reason sexuality becomes such a major concern for men with SCIs is that the American culture has conditioned men into believing that their self-worth and self-esteem are measured by their physical strength, body image, and sexual abilities. Men who are unable to live up to these standards are then considered undesirable. This is a myth and stereotype that, if acceped, can affect how men see themselves and how we relate to others.

The early research on sexuality and males with SCIs centered on issues pertaining to erectile dysfunction, sperm quality, and fertility. All other issues relating to sexuality were ignored or avoided. As a result, it was the responsibility of individuals to address sexuality concerns and issues on their own. The extent of sexual impairment as the result of a SCI depends on the level of the injury. If sexuality issues are not addressed during the rehabilitation process, there is a possibility that the individual's emotional well being as well as how he relates to others could suffer. Men with spinal cord injuries need to learn that in order to develop a satisfying and healthy sex life following their injury they must be willing to change and redefine their expectations of the sexual experience. A positive sexual adjustment can improve an individual's overall outlook on life. It can be the difference between becoming socially involved or socially withdrawn.

I would like to share with you the story behind the title of this manual, "Is Fred Dead?" When I was a young boy, as with many young boys, it was difficult and embarrassing to talk to my parents or others about my penis. Talking to my mother about my penis just didn't seem right. So to avoid this embarrassment, I gave my penis a name, Fred. At the time of my diving accident I was seventeen years old and one big mass of raging hormones wanting to find a release. Girls and dating had become one of my favorite past-times. Although I had not had sexual intercourse, I was looking forward to my first experience. My father, who was concerned for my welfare, wanted to be sure that I was well protected and made me carry a rubber in my wallet just in case the opportunity presented itself. This rubber was never used but it did leave a nice lasting circular impression on the outside of my leather wallet. A couple of days following my injury, as I lay face up staring at the ceiling and unable to move my body in the ICU of Toronto Medical Center, I thought to myself that my sex life was over. My desire and dream to be sexually active with a woman of my age was vanishing.

When my parents arrived after a long drive from Pennsylvania, one of the first things that I said to my mother was, "Fred is dead." I had all these beautiful young nurses working on me, and I was unable to have an erection. When I became stable enough to be transported, I was flown from Canada back to the United States and transferred to the SCI Unit at Shriner's Hospital for Children in Philadelphia. While at Shriner's, I had a beautiful young nurse named Mary Claire. Every time she walked into the room she mentally excited me, however, physically nothing happened. I was so frustrated that I became very depressed. I felt my manhood was gone. Then one day as Mary Claire was putting on an external catheter, all of a sudden I got an erection. It was so hard and erect that I was both embarrassed and excited at the same time. Fred was back. He was still alive! I couldn't wait to tell my mother. I later learned that what I had was a reflexagenic erection. I didn't care what it was called, the fact was that I was able to have an erection. I started to think maybe there was still a chance for my dream to come true. Maybe I could be sexually active after all.

My only disappointment with my rehabilitation was that it lacked usable information about sexuality. My introduction to sexuality with a spinal cord injury consisted of watching the movie, 'Coming Home', and receiving handouts on sexually transmitted diseases and electroejaculation. Everything I learned about having sex with a SCI, I had to learn on my own. Having a spinal cord injury doesn't mean your sex life is over. In fact, it's just beginning. You have to believe in yourself and feel sexually attractive. This is the first step in becoming sexually involved with another person.

This manual is written specifically for men with spinal cord injuries. The purpose of this manual is to educate men and their partners about sexuality following a SCI. The manual can be read as part of one's rehabilitation treatment or independently to increase one's awareness and understanding of issues relating to sexuality and living with a spinal cord injury. The information in this manual is intended to be shared by couples to increase their awareness and to help them experience each other sexually at a greater level of intimacy. Each chapter in this manual builds upon the one before. I feel it is better to develop a good solid foundation by beginning with the basics and then moving on from there. Chapter 1 provides a basic overview of spinal anatomy and discusses the types of spinal cord injuries. Chapter 2 explains the male and female sexual anatomy and explores the sexual cycle. Chapter 3 focuses on issues relating to dating, relationships, and learning how to communicate effectively with your partner. The issue of erectile dysfunction and fertility are explored in chapters 4 and 5. The topics that are often neglected in most programs on sexuality with a SCI such as oral sex, sexual positions, and the use of sexual aides are all explored in great detail in chapters 6, 7, and 8. Finally, no manual on sexuality would be complete without a discussion about sexually transmitted diseases (STD) and how to properly use a condom. This is in Chapter 9. Having a SCI does not protect you from getting a STD. No one ever thinks they will catch a STD, but they can. I don't know anyone that wants a STD or HIV/AIDS. My hope is that by reading this manual men who sustain a spinal cord injury will be able to develop their sexuality and live a more enriched life with their partner.

Dr. Robert W. Baer

Chapter 1
The Spinal Anatomy

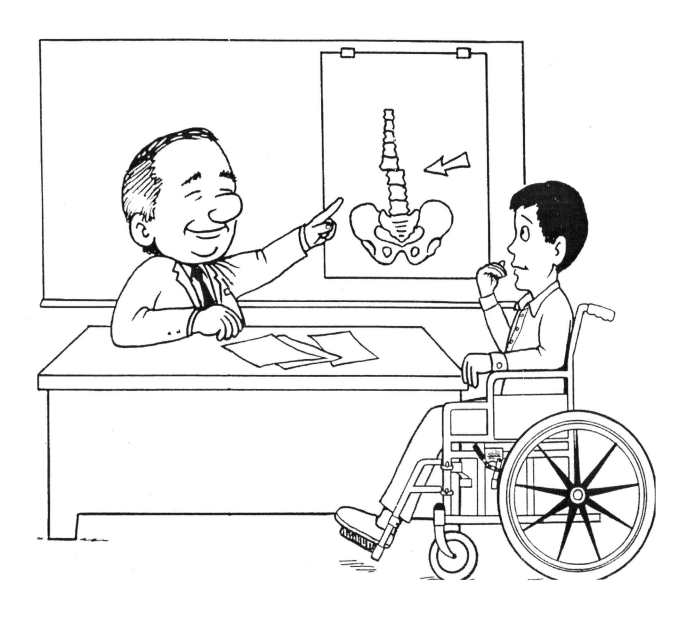

The purpose of this chapter is to introduce you to the anatomy of the spinal cord. This can help you better understand what the spinal cord does, how it is protected, and the types of spinal cord injuries that can occur. The spinal cord is part of the central nervous system, which consists of the brain and the spinal cord. The brain is the command center of the body, performing literally thousands of functions all at the same time. We are unaware that most of these functions are occurring. The brain performs many tasks including thinking, remembering, and maintaining the internal environment of the body. The brain also receives information from the body, makes decisions, and tells the body how to respond. It sends and receives information to and from the body through the spinal cord and spinal nerves.

The spinal cord is very similar to the information highway transporting thousands of messages a second throughout the body. Some messages are slower than others while some are sent via express. From the spinal cord, the messages branch off at various spinal nerves similar to exits off a major interstate highway where they proceed to their final destination. Let's imagine you just stubbed your big toe on a step. A message is sent from your big toe up the nerve in your leg, through the spinal nerve, up the spinal cord, and into your brain. The message received is lots of pain. The brain responds by sending a message down to the big toe to pull the foot back and then sends a few choice words to your vocal cords. These messages are sent and received within a fraction of a second. Damage to the spinal cord anywhere along the way can severely or permanently disrupt the passage of information between the brain and other parts of the body. We will further explore the spinal cord below.

The Spinal Anatomy

The Spinal Cord: As stated above, the spinal cord makes up part of the central nervous system. The spinal cord begins at the base of the brain at the foramen magnum, extends down the spinal canal, and ends at approximately the first or second lumbar vertebra. The end of the spinal cord tapers to a cone known as the conus medullaris. In adults the spinal cord is approximately 18 inches in length.

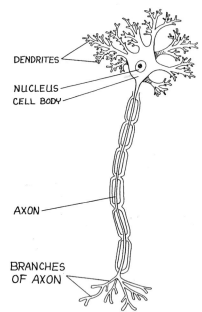

If one would look at a cross section of the spinal cord, he/she would discover that the cord is divided into two distinct areas. The outer area of the spinal cord consists of myelinated nerve fibers called white matter. A myelinated nerve has a type of insulation around it allowing it to send information through the body faster. The inner area of the spinal cord consists of the cell bodies of neurons called gray matter.

A single neuron (nerve cell) from the spinal cord consists of three parts: the dendrites, the cell body, and the axon (see Figure 1.1). The dendrites receive information from other nerves, the cell body reacts to the message being passed, and the axon continues to transfer the message to other nerves. The spinal cord consists of thousands of these nerve cells working together to transfer information to and from the brain and other areas of the body. Overall, the spinal cord is considered to be the largest nerve network in the body. Because of its importance, the body has constructed a bony fortress to protect it from harm. This protective fortress is known as the spine.

Figure 1.1 Neuron

The Spine: The spine or vertebral column consists of 33 individual and fused vertebrae. It is divided into five regions: cervical, thoracic, lumbar, sacral, and coccyx. In adults the cervical, thoracic, and lumbar regions are flexible vertebrae, meaning they can move freely, whereas the sacral and coccyx are fused together forming what is commonly known as the tailbone.

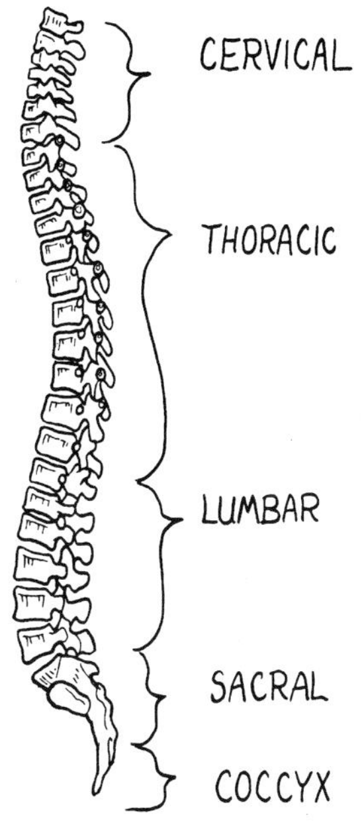

The Vertebrae: The spinal column consists of 7 cervical, 12 thoracic, 5 lumbar, 5 fused sacral and 4 fused coccyx vertebrae (see Figure 1.2). The vertebrae, with the exception of the first vertebra, are similar in structure. The anterior portion of a vertebra consists of the body, and the posterior portion consists of the arch. The arch is made out of a pair of pedicles, a pair of laminae, and seven processes. The vertebrae, when stacked one on top of the other, form a hollow bony canal called the spinal canal, which provides passage for the spinal cord.

Figure 1.2
Side View of Spinal
Column

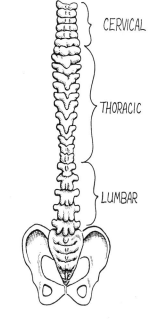

Figure 1.3
Front View of
Spinal Column

The vertebrae generally increase in size as they descend down the spinal column, which allows the spine to bear an increase in weight lifting capabilities (see Figure 1.3). In addition to differences in size, each of the seven vertebra regions performs a different function. The thoracic vertebrae allow for powerful flexion and some extension. The lumbar vertebrae have somewhat limited movement, whereas the vertebrae located in the cervical region allow for flexion, extension, and rotation of the head. When comparing the flexibility of the vertebral column, the cervical vertebrae allow for maximum movement, especially between C4 and C6. As a result, this area of the vertebral column is where most spinal cord injuries occur (Zejdlik, 1992).

The vertebrae are separated by individual intervertebral cartilaginous discs, also called ligaments. These discs have a hard outer shell and a soft gelatin center which enables them to act as tiny shock absorbers to assist the spine with weight bearing activities.

The Spinal Nerves: The spinal nerves branch out from the spinal cord and, along with the cranial nerves, form the systematic nervous system. There are 31 pairs of spinal nerves including 8 cervical, 12 thoracic, 5 lumbar, 5 sacral, and 1 coccygeal nerve. The spinal cord has two types of message carrying nerve fibers. Efferent nerves carry motor information, and afferent nerves send sensory information from the body to the brain making it aware of the external environment. For more detailed information about the spine and the spinal cord it is recommended that you speak with a physician or a rehabilitation specialist.

Types of Spinal Cord Injuries

A spinal cord injury can occur at any level of the spinal column. Injuries and fractures to the spine can differ in severity and may or may not affect the spinal cord. Spinal cord injuries are classified as:

- Flexion Injuries.
- Hyperextension Injuries.
- Rotation Injuries.
- Compression Injuries

Flexion Injuries: Flexion injuries (see Figure 1.4) occur when the spinal cord is violently thrust forward or sideways such as during a head-on collision in an automobile accident or falling from a horse, motorcycle, ATV, etc. This type of injury can involve nerve damage, broken vertebrae, torn ligaments, and a misalignment of the spinal column.

Hyperextension Injuries: A hyperextension injury (see Figure 1.5) occurs when the spinal cord in violently bent backwards, such as in a rear-end collision in

FLEXION INJURY

Figure 1.4

HYPEREXTENSION INJURY

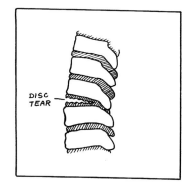

BAM!

Figure 1.5

an automobile accident or when older adults fall forward and hit their chin or head on an object such as a sink or table. A hyperextension injury can also result in nerve damage, broken vertebrae, torn ligaments, and a misalignment of the spinal column.

Rotation Injuries: Rotation injuries (see Figure 1.6) occur when the spinal cord is violently thrust in two different directions at the same time. An example would be an automobile accident where the car is hit from the side causing the body to turn in the opposite direction from the head, twisting the spine or falling down a staircase. This type of injury can result in ruptured discs, fractured vertebrae, and stretched or severed nerves.

ROTATION INJURY

DISC TEAR

VERTEBRAE FRACTURE

Figure 1.6

Compression Injuries: Compression injuries (see Figure 1.7) are the result of a vertical compression of the spinal column. This is the typical injury that occurs when an individual dives into a shallow body of water such as a lake or swimming pool. The head hits the bottom or some other hard object under the surface of the water like a rock or a submerged log. This type of injury can produce crushed vertebrae and severed nerves.

Complete versus Incomplete Spinal Cord Injuries

Complete Spinal Cord Injuries: In addition to being classified by type, a spinal cord injury is also classified as either complete or incomplete. A complete spinal cord injury means there is total damage to the spinal cord. This results in the individual losing all sensation and movement below the level of the injury.

Incomplete Spinal Cord Injuries: An incomplete spinal cord injury means that the damage to the spinal cord was incomplete or partial. This means the individual has some degree of movement and/or sensations below the level of the injury.

The Location of the Spinal Cord Injury

When individuals talk about someone who has had a spinal cord injury, they often refer to them as a quadriplegic or a paraplegic. There are some individuals who have gotten into the bad habit of referring to everyone with a spinal cord injury as a paraplegic. This is similar to going to a restaurant where the waitress refers to all the soft drinks they serve as Coke. There is a difference. The location of the injury to the spinal cord determines the severity of

COMPRESSION INJURY

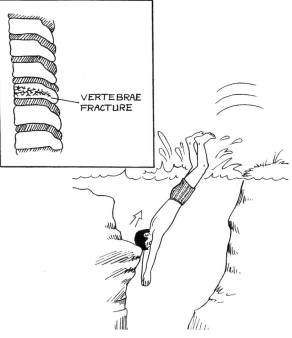

VERTEBRAE FRACTURE

Figure 1.7

function loss. The higher the lesion on the spinal cord, the greater the loss of sensation and bodily function. Individuals with spinal cord injuries with damage between C1 and T1 are often referred to as quadriplegics, meaning they have sustained paralysis in all four limbs. Individuals with spinal cord injuries below T1, in the thoracic, lumbar, sacral, or coccygeal regions, are referred to as paraplegics. These individuals have sustained paralysis of the lower extremities including the lower trunk.

Level of functioning following a spinal cord injury

The individual's level of functioning following a spinal cord injury depends on how severe the damage is to the spinal cord. Most damage to the spinal cord is the result of swelling and bruising of the spinal nerves. In addition, function depends on whether the injury is complete or incomplete. The following is a brief overview of the bodily functions and activity levels at the various locations of the spine that can be affected by a spinal cord injury in that region:

C1-C3:
- The diaphragm does not function therefore a respirator is needed to aid in breathing. These individuals may have difficulty speaking.
- The individual has the ability to move the head and neck. However, a person with a complete injure will lose movement and function in the lower extremities (arms and legs).
- Feelings and sensations are centered around the face, neck, and possibly the shoulder areas.
- There is no control over bowel or bladder functioning.
- **There is impaired sexual functioning.**
- The individual is totally dependent on others for self-care including feeding, dressing, grooming, and bathing.
- He/she is able to use a specialized power wheelchair with head, breath, or mouth controls.

C4:
- The individual is able to breathe on his/her own without the aid of a respirator.
- He/she has the ability to use head, neck, and shoulder muscles.
- There is feeling and sensation in the face, neck, and shoulders.
- He/she has no control over bowel or bladder functioning.
- **There is impaired sexual functioning.**
- The individual is totally dependent on others for self-care.
- He/she is able to use a special adapted power wheelchair.

C5:
- These individuals have the ability to use head, neck, and shoulder muscles along with the bicep muscles in the arms for elbow flexion.
- There is feeling and sensation in the face, neck, shoulders, and upper chest area.
- He/she has no control over bowel or bladder functioning.
- **There is impaired sexual functioning.**
- The individual is dependent on others for self-care (dressing, bathing, cooking…).
- The individual is able to feed and groom themselves using adaptive equipment and assistance from others.
- The individual is capable of transferring using a sliding board and assistance.

- The individual can push a manual wheelchair short and level distances. They may prefer a power wheelchair for traveling long distances outdoors, to pursue vocational opportunities, or during poor weather conditions such as rain or snow.
- He/she is able to drive a van using adaptive equipment.

C6:
- The individual has head, neck, shoulder and scapular muscles.
- He/she has elbow flexion and wrist extension.
- There is feeling and sensation in the face, neck, shoulders, and mid-chest area.
- He/she has no control over bowel or bladder functioning. However, they may be able to perform their own bowel and bladder care with some assistance.
- **There is impaired sexual functioning.**
- These individuals are capable of eating, grooming, dressing, and bathing.
- He/she can transfer with or without a sliding board independently.
- He/she can cook and perform light housework.
- The individual can use a manual wheelchair.
- Able to drive a van using adaptive equipment.
- He/she can live independently with outside support such as an attendant care agency.

C7:
- The individual has motion in their head, neck, shoulder and scapular muscles.
- The individual has the use of bicep and weakened tricep muscles of the arms along with elbow flexion and weak elbow extensior, wrist extension and flexion, and limited flexion and extension of the fingers.
- He/she has feeling and sensation in the face, neck, shoulders, and chest.
- Has no control over bowel or bladder functioning but able to perform self-care.
- **There is impaired sexual functioning.**
- The individual is able to perform all the daily tasks listed above for C6 but with less difficulty.
- The individual can use a manual wheelchair.
- Is able to drive a van using adaptive equipment.
- Can live independently.

T1:
- Has the use of all upper extremity muscles.
- May have some difficulty with balance.
- Has no control over bowel or bladder functioning but able to perform self-care.
- **There is impaired sexual functioning.**
- Can live independently and perform household chores.
- Has use of a manual wheelchair.
- Able to drive a van or car using adaptive hand controls.

T2-T12:
- Has increased respiratory and abdominal muscle functioning.
- Has no control over bowel or bladder functioning, but able to perform self-care.
- **Has impaired sexual functioning.**
- Able to live independently and perform household chores.
- Has use of a manual wheelchair.

- Can stand using long leg braces for support.
- Is able to drive a car using adaptive hand controls.

L1-S1:
- These individuals have use of the upper extremity muscles and the abdominal muscles. An injury to this area of the spine affects the hip and lower leg muscles.
- They will experience complications with bowel or bladder functioning.
- **There will be impaired sexual functioning.**
- These individuals can be trained how to walk using leg and knee bracing for support.

S2-S4:
- These individuals have the use of upper and lower extremity muscles. However, they may experience some weakness within the lower leg and foot.
- They will experience complications with bowel or bladder functioning.
- **There will be impaired sexual functioning.**
- They often require some type of minimal bracing to assist in standing and walking.

Please note that each spinal cord injury is unique and the activity level and function impairment may vary from those listed above. Now that you have read the basics of spinal anatomy and spinal cord injuries, I hope that one reoccurring theme popped out at you. No matter where one has a spinal cord injury, there is going to be some type of impairment in sexual functioning. The chapters that follow will explore the major issues related to sexuality following a spinal cord injury.

Suggested Readings and Resources

Buchanan, L. E. & Nawoczenski, D. A. (1987). "Spinal Cord Injury" Concepts and Management Approaches, Baltimore: Williams & Wilkins.

Seeley, R. R., Stephens, T. D., & Tate, P. (2000). Anatomy & Physiology. (5th Ed) New York: McGraw Hill.

Senelick, R. C., & Dougherty, K., (1998). The Spinal Cord Injury Handbook for Patients and Their Families. Birmingham, Alabama: HealthSouth Press.

Zejdlik, C. P. (1992). Management of Spinal Cord Injuries. (2nd Ed) Boston: Jones & Barlett Publishers, Inc.

Chapter 2
Sexual Anatomy & the Body's Response

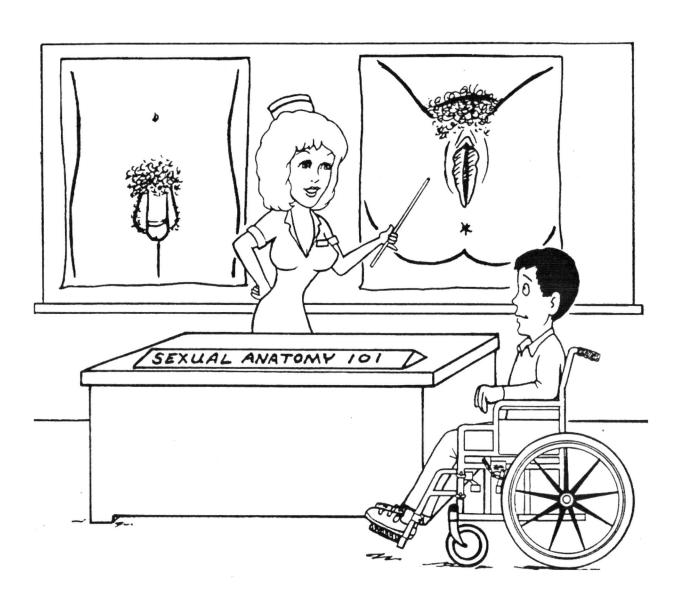

Before we dive into the wonderful and exciting world of sexuality with a spinal cord injury, we must first look at some basic information regarding the male and female sexual anatomy. We will also explore the stages of the sexual response cycle. The purpose of this chapter is not to make you an expert on sexual anatomy, but instead to make you a better and more sensitive lover. Think about it for a second. Would you take your favorite red Corvette to someone who has no knowledge of how the parts of an engine function or how they go together? I don't think so. Nor would others want you to fix their cars if you knew nothing about car repair or how to fine-tune an engine to make it a smooth-running machine. Becoming a good lover is similar to being a good mechanic; you need to know where the parts are, how they function, and how to make them work together to get peak performance.

When you finish reading this chapter, you will be able to answer these questions: What physiological changes occur in the body during each stage of the sexual response cycle? Where are the erogenous zones of the male and female body? What areas of the vulva are the most sensitive to stimulation? What is the most sensitive area of the penis? Knowing this information can help you and your partner become more aware of how each of you is responding to stimulation. You'll be able to tell by her body's response how near she is to having an orgasm. But most importantly, knowing the information in this chapter will assist you in communicating your needs and desires to your partner and vise versa.

Some important information to keep in mind is that everyone's body is different. Therefore, sexual organs will differ in size, shape, and color. An individual's sexual organs can also have a different level of sensitivity. This is why it is important to become acquainted with both your own and your partner's sexual organs and their sensitivity. By knowing your partner's most sensitive areas, your lovemaking will be much more rewarding.

First, we will explore the female and then the male sexual anatomy. Next, we will discuss what changes occur to our bodies as we become sexually aroused, what occurs during an orgasm, and what happens to the body afterwards. Finally, we will explore the erogenous zones of both bodies. The human sexual organs are often referred to as the **genitals**. The genitals are actually only part of the male and female sexual organs. They consist of the external sexual organs found in the pelvic region. The male's genitals consist of the penis and the scrotum. The female's genitals include the vulva and the opening of the vagina.

The Female Sexual Anatomy

One of the first steps for a male to become an effective lover is to become familiar with the female sexual organs. The female sexual organs can be divided into the external sexual organs and the internal sexual organs.

The Female External Sexual Organs

The Vulva: The external sexual organs of a woman are known as the **vulva**, which means covering. The vulva consists of the mons pubis, the labia majora, the labia minora, the clitoris, and the perineum (see Figure 2.1). The vulva is a very sensitive area of a woman's body because of the high concentration of nerve endings. The purpose of the vulva is to protect the openings of the urethra and the vagina.

The Mons Pubis: The mons pubis, also known as the mons veneris (pubic mound or the mound of venus), is located in the front of the vulva. The mons pubis consists of fatty tissue and skin which is usually covered with pubic hair. The mons pubis forms a cushion over the pubic bone and provides protection for the sexual organs. This area is known to be rich in nerve endings making it sensitive to the touch. A woman may find direct stimulation to this area quite pleasurable and sexually arousing.

The Labia Majora (the outer lips): The labia majora consist of fatty tissue and muscles that protect the sides of the woman's external sexual organs and the openings to the vagina and the urethra. They contain hair follicles, apocrine glands, and sebaceous glands. They are also rich in sensitive nerve endings. The **apocrine glands** are sweat glands which produce a natural aroma that most men find very attractive and sexually stimulating. The **sebaceous glands** are oil glands that produce a natural form

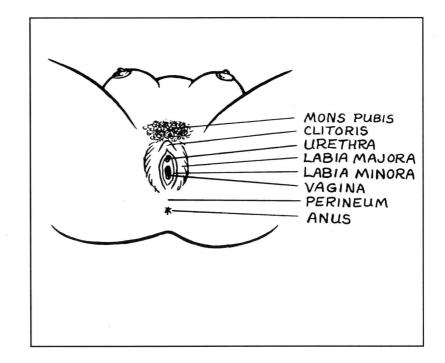

Figure 2.1 The Female External Sexual Organs

of lubrication known as **sebum**. This helps to lubricate the vagina. It is interesting to note that the left side of a woman's labia majora is usually larger than the right side.

The Labia Minora (the inner lips): The labia minora consist of two inner folds of soft, spongy skin located inside the labia majora. They surround the clitoris and the openings of the vagina and urethra. The labia minora are hairless because they do not contain any hair follicles; instead, they contain many sebaceous glands. They are full of nerve endings making them very sensitive to touch, temperature, and pressure. The two labia minora come together above the clitoris, forming what is known as the clitoral hood. When a woman is sexually excited, her labia minora will become engorged, change color, and increase in thickness. The labia minora can actually expand as much as two or three times their normal size. In a non-aroused state one side of the labia minora is usually larger than the other.

The Clitoris: The clitoris is the most sensitive part of the female's sex organs because it contains many receptive nerve endings. The clitoris is located below the mons pubis beneath the clitoral hood. It looks like a small shiny button about the size of a pea. The clitoris serves only one purpose - to give sexual pleasure to the woman when it is stimulated. The clitoris consists of parts similar to the penis and has, in fact, been called the female's equivalent of the penis. During sexual arousal the clitoris will double in size and become erect just like the penis.

The Opening of the Urethra: The opening of the urethra is located between the clitoris and the opening of the vagina. Its purpose is to allow for the passage of urine from the bladder. The urethra has no sexual

11

function nor is it a part of the reproductive system.

The Perineum: The perineum is the area between the vagina and the anus; it is located at the back of the vulva. It contains no hair follicles but has many nerve endings which, when stimulated, can be a source of sexual arousal. The perineum is sensitive to touch, temperature, and pressure.

The Female Internal Sex Organs

The Vagina: The vagina is the muscular canal that extends from the vaginal opening to the cervix, located at the base of the uterus. The tissue located around the opening of the vagina is known as the **introitus**. The vagina can vary in length between 3 ½ to 5 inches. The vagina has three functions: it allows for passage of the woman's menstrual flow, it receives the penis during intercourse, and it is the canal through which a baby passes during the birth process. During times of nonsexual arousal, the walls of the vagina lie flat against each other like a deflated balloon (see Figure 2.2). However, when an object such as a penis, a finger, or a vibrator is inserted into the vagina, the muscles of the vagina can expand and contract to accommodate the size and shape of the object.

The Hymen: The opening of the vagina can be covered by a thin flap of skin known as the hymen. The hymen can cover part or all of the vaginal opening. It can be of different sizes, shapes, and thickness. The hymen has no known function. An old myth in our society is that if a woman has an intact hymen, she is a virgin. This is not necessarily true. In fact, some women are born without a hymen. A woman's hymen can break during her youth, especially if she is active in sports. A hymen can also break from inserting a tampon into the vagina. If the woman's hymen is intact, it will break during her first intercourse, which may or may not be the cause of any pain or discomfort. Many women do experience pain during their first intercourse, although it may be related to the pelvic floor muscles instead of the hymen.

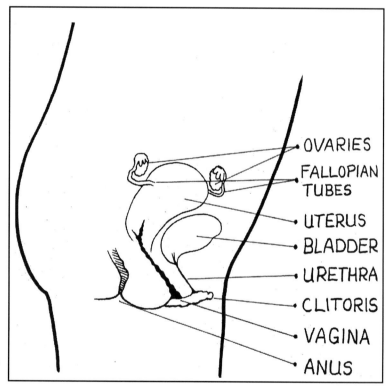

Figure 2.2 Female Internal Sexual Organs

The G-Spot: The G-Spot, also known as the Grafenberg Spot, was named after Dr. Enrst Grafenberg, a German gynecologist who first discovered the area in the early 1950s. The G-Spot is located on the front wall of the vagina near the navel approximately an inch or two from the vaginal opening. When stimulated, the area swells resulting in a deeply intense uteral orgasm. Some women have reported experiencing a release of fluid through their urethra resembling a male ejaculation. Researchers are unclear as to the actual content of this fluid, however some researchers conclude that the fluid is urine released at the time of the orgasm.

The best positions for locating the G-Spot is with the woman sitting, squatting, or kneeling. It is rather difficult to locate the G-Spot if the woman is lying down. Insert two fingers into the vagina and begin stroking the front wall of the vagina while exerting firm upward pressure. Once you have successfully located the G-Spot, as you continue to stimulate the area, you will notice that it begins to swell. Repeated stimulation will cause your partner to experience deep contractions that originate from within her uterus and sweep outward. The result is that your partner will experience a deep uteral orgasm instead of a vulva orgasm (Berger, 1988). For further information regarding the G-Spot, see suggested readings at the end of this chapter.

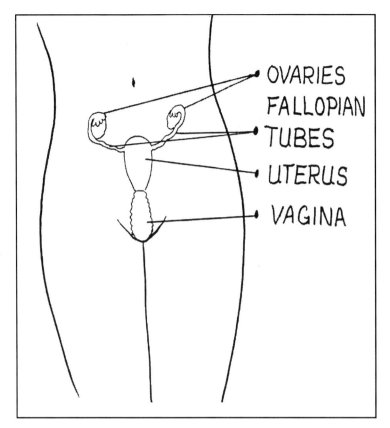

Figure 2.3 Female Reproductive Organs

The Uterus: The uterus, also known as the womb, is the upside-down, pear-shaped organ about the size of your closed fist. It is located above the vagina (see Figure 2.3). The uterus is where a fetus develops. The bottom of the uterus is called the cervix, which extends slightly into the vagina. During intercourse the penis may actually hit the cervix, which can be pleasurable to some women or painful and uncomfortable to others.

The Fallopian Tubes: The fallopian tubes are located on both sides of the uterus and serve as a passageway for the mature egg to travel from the ovaries to the uterus. The fallopian tubes consist of thousands of **cilia,** which look like small hairs that move the egg along toward the uterus.

The Ovaries: Women have two ovaries, located on each side of the body. The ovaries are where the eggs are stored until they mature. For further information regarding human reproduction, see suggested readings at the end of this chapter.

The Male Sexual Anatomy

When one considers the male sexual anatomy, the penis is the most recognized of all the sexual organs. The main reason for this recognition is that throughout their lives boys and men handle their penis on a daily basis every time they urinate. Boys are taught at a young age through stories and jokes that their penis isn't just for urinating. The male's sexual anatomy also contains external and internal sexual organs.

The Male's External Sexual Organs:

The Penis: The penis actually has dual functions: it provides a passageway for urine to leave the body, and it has a reproductive purpose allowing a man to deposit his semen into a woman's vagina. The penis is divided into two sections, the **shaft** and the **glans** (see Figure 2.4). The shaft of the penis is the long tube that connects to the body at one end and to the glans at the other. The shaft of the penis is very sensitive to touch, pressure, and temperature. Internally, the shaft of the penis consists of three parallel cylinders of soft spongy tissue that are covered by a thick membrane known as the foreskin. The cylinder located on the underside of the penis is known as the **corpus spongiosum**. In the center of the corpus spongiosum is the **urethra**. The urethra is a hollow tube that runs from the bladder and exits at the urethral opening located at the center of the glans. The urethra provides a passageway for urine and semen to exit the body. Located on each side of the shaft of the penis are two identical cylinders known as the **corpus cavernosa**.

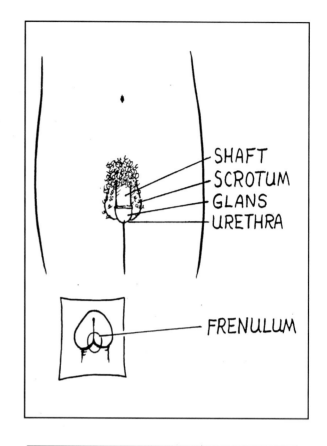

Figure 2.4 Male External Sexual Organs

During times of non-sexual excitement, blood flows freely through the tissues of the corpus spongiosum and the corpus cavernosa. However, when the penis is stimulated, such as during sexual activity, tiny muscles in the corpus spongiosum and corpus cavernosa relax allowing blood to enter into the spongy tissue causing an erection. Once the stimulation discontinues, these muscles tighten, closing the caverns and allowing the blood to return to the bloodstream. As a result, the penis softens and returns to its normal flaccid state.

The **glans** of the penis, also known as the tip or the head, consists entirely of corpus spongiosum tissue. The glans is highly sensitive to physical touch because it has a higher concentration of nerve endings than does the shaft. In fact, some men find that direct simulation to their glans is rather painful; as a result, they prefer physical stimulation of the shaft of the penis. Two other areas of the glans which are highly sensitive to direct stimulation are the coronal ridge and the frenulum (see Figure 2.4). The **coronal ridge** is the rim of skin which separates the glans from the shaft of the penis. The **frenulum**, located on the underside of the penis, is a small thin triangular region of skin where the glans and the shaft join.

All penises at birth are covered by a loose fold of skin known as the **foreskin** that protects the glans. It has become common practice in the United States and in some religions that the foreskin be surgically removed at birth. A penis that has had the foreskin removed is known as a **circumcised penis**. A penis that has not had the foreskin removed is called an **uncircumcised penis**. The advantage of a circumcised penis is primarily related to issues of good health and hygiene. However, men with uncircumcised penises can easily prevent the growth of unwanted bacteria, which can grow in between the folds of skin, by maintaining good hygiene habits through daily cleaning of the penis.

The Scrotum: The scrotum is the sac of skin that hangs below the penis. Inside the scrotum are two ball-shaped glands known as the testes (see Figure 2.5). The function of the scrotum is to protect the testes and to maintain a proper environment that will promote sperm production. In order to produce sperm, the testes must maintain a certain temperature. The scrotum maintains this stable temperature by the distance it hangs from the body. If the testes need more heat, the scrotum pulls closer to the body. If there is too much heat for the testes, the scrotum will lengthen and hang further away from the body. This explains why the scrotum shrinks whenever you swim in cold water or hangs low from the body following a hot shower. The name of the muscle that is responsible for raising or lowering the scrotum is the **cremaster muscle,** and the process of adjusting the scrotum is known as the **cremaster reflex.**

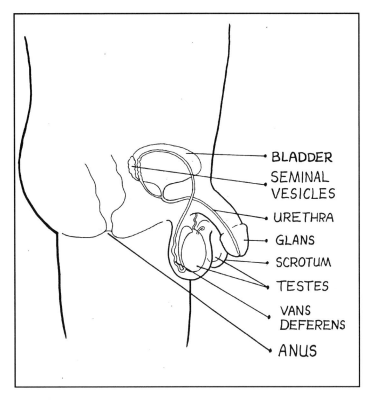

Figure 2.5 Male Internal Sexual Organs

The Male's Internal Sexual Organs

The Testes: The testes (located inside the scrotum) have two functions: they produce sex hormones known as androgens, and they produce sperm. The most important of the androgens produced by the testes is testosterone, which is responsible for the male's sexual development as he matures. The testes are comprised of a network of tightly coiled tubes known as the **seminiferous tubules**. It is in these seminiferous tubules where sperm is produced. The process of producing sperm is known as **spermatogenesis**, a process that takes an average of 70 days. A man will produce sperm from puberty until death, producing billions of sperm annually.

The Epididymis: As the sperm begin to mature, they move from the seminiferous tubules into the epididymis, which are the coiled tubes located at the top of each testes. The sperm once in the epididymis continue to mature and gain the ability to swim. The epididymis stores the mature sperm until they are released from the body during the peak period of sexual excitement known as an ejaculation.

The Vas Deferens: Before the fully matured sperm exit the body during ejaculation, they are transferred from the epididymis to the seminal vesicles by a thin tube known as the vas deferens.

The Seminal Vesicles: The seminal vesicles are two small organs located below the bladder. The purpose of this organ is to add 70% of a milky fluid to the sperm known as seminal fluid. This fluid provides the sperm with nourishment and helps to ease sperm movement through the male urethra and the vagina.

The Prostate Gland: The prostate gland is located below the bladder and is about the size of a chestnut. The urethra passes directly through the prostate gland. Prior to ejaculation, the sperm are transferred from the seminal vesicles to the prostate gland. The prostate gland, at the time of ejaculation, secretes the remaining 30% of the seminal fluid into the urethra.

The Cowper's Glands: Located just beyond the prostate is a pair of glands known as the Cowper's glands. These glands are responsible for adding lubrication to the seminal fluid prior to ejaculation.

The Male's Orgasm: During the height of sexual excitement ejaculation occurs when the prostate muscles open and the prostate pumps the seminal fluid and sperm through the urethra and out its opening. It is not possible for urine and sperm to mix whenever a man urinates because muscles in the prostate prevent this from occurring. Also, when the penis is erect, the bladder is closed so that urine cannot be released into the urethra as the sperm pass through. However, there are situations, such as when an individual has a spinal cord injury that these muscles do not function as they should. What often occurs when these muscles are not functioning is that instead of sperm exiting the body, it is ejaculated into the bladder, a condition known as a retrograde ejaculation, which will be discussed further in Chapter 5 – Male Fertility following an SCI.

The Sexual Response Cycle

Before we begin to explore the changes in sexual functioning following a spinal cord injury we must first understand the sexual response cycle of individuals without a SCI. In 1966 Masters and Johnson conducted a study of the sexual physiological response of humans. The subjects for this study included 382 women and 312 men. The findings of this study concluded that the human body cycles through four stages of sexual arousal. These four stages include excitement, plateau, orgasm, and resolution. It must be noted that there are no distinct boundaries between one stage and the next. The stages tend to flow into each other. Also, in order to be sexually satisfied, not everyone has to reach the orgasm stage. There is no preset amount of time that one needs to be in each of the stages. At times a person may progress through the stages quickly, such as when having a "quickie." Other times he/she may progress through the stages more slowly, such as an evening with a partner going out to dinner, maybe doing some dancing or wheeling through the park, followed by some hugging and kissing that ends with a full sexual encounter. In both cases the body progresses through the same stages but at different rates. There will also be times when an individual's body will start through any of the first three stages but have to discontinue the process because something unexpected happens. The body recovers and returns to its normal state of arousal (Masters, Johnson, & Kolodny, 1995). We will briefly look at these stages and the changes that occur in the body during each of them.

Excitement Stage: The first stage of the sexual response cycle. Excitement occurs as the body responds to some type of sexual stimulation, which can be in the form of physical touch or psychological image, in both men and women. We can use our senses such as taste, smell, sight, and hearing to enhance our feelings of excitement during this stage.

Body changes that occur in both men and women during the excitement stage:

- Increase in heart rate, blood pressure, and rate of breathing.
- Tensing of the muscles.
- "Sex flush," which is the reddening, spotty, or rash-like coloring of the skin that usually occurs around the areas of the breasts, neck, and chest.
- The nipples become erect.

Changes specific to the woman's body during the excitement stage:
- The first sign women experience is vaginal lubrication.
- The inner two thirds of the vagina expand as the cervix and the uterus rise slightly.
- The breasts begin to increase in size.
- The clitoris swells and becomes enlarged.
- The labia majora flatten and separate.
- The labia minora begin to enlarge.

Changes specific in the man's body during the excitement stage:
- The penis becomes erect.
- The scrotum thickens and brings the testes closer to the body.

Plateau Stage: The second stage of the sexual response cycle. It is at this point where the high level of physiological arousal is maintained as the body prepares for the orgasm. This stage can differ in duration depending on the individual's level of stimulation necessary to achieve an orgasm.

Body changes in both men and women during the plateau stage:
- The heart rate and blood pressure continue to increase.
- Breathing becomes more rapid.
- The muscles in the body tense causing the possibility of muscle spasms.
- Sex flush continues around the area of the abdomen, breasts, neck, and chest.

Changes specific to the woman's body during the plateau stage:
- The production of vaginal fluid often slows during this stage.
- The clitoris retracts beneath the clitoral hood as it moves back toward the pubic bone.
- Late in this stage the areolas around the nipples become larger and breast size increases.
- The labia majora continue to spread apart as the labia minora swell giving greater access to the vaginal opening.

Changes specific in the man's body during the plateau stage:
- The Cowper's glands secrete pre-ejaculation fluid.
- The glans increases in diameter and may change to a darker shade of red because of a high concentration of blood in the area.
- The testes enlarge and continue to move closer to the body until they come to rest on the perineum.

Orgasm Stage: The third stage of the sexual response cycle. If stimulation continues throughout the plateau stage a point will be reached where the body will release the build up of sexual tension resulting in an orgasm.

Body changes in both men and women during the orgasm stage:
- The heart rate, breathing, and blood pressure reach their highest rate in this stage.

- The sex flush continues to spread to other areas of the body.
- There is a loss of muscle control and an increase in muscle spasms.
- There are contractions in the anus and pelvic muscles.

Changes specific to the woman's body during the orgasm stage:
- The woman will experience contractions in the vagina and the uterus.

Changes specific to the man's body during the orgasm stage:
- Ejaculation of semen occurs.

Resolution Stage: The fourth and final stage of the sexual response cycle. There tends to be a difference in the sexual response between men and women following an orgasm. Women tend to be able to have multiple orgasms. What this means is that women are able to experience orgasms one after another as long as the level of stimulation does not fall below the plateau level of arousal. Men, on the other hand, are only able to experience one orgasm followed by a refractory period. During this refractory period there is no chance of the male experiencing an orgasm or an ejaculation. This period can last from several minutes up to several hours. Usually as men age, the refractory period becomes longer. The physiological events that occur during the resolution stage are opposite those that occur during the excitement and the plateau stages.

Body changes in both men and women during the resolution stage:
- Heart rate and blood pressure returns to a normal state.
- The nipples are no longer erect.
- The body sweats.

Changes specific to the woman's body during the resolution stage:
- The breasts and areolas decrease in size.
- The clitoris decreases in size.
- The labia decrease in size and return to a lighter color.
- The opening of the cervix remains open for 20 to 30 minutes in order to allow the sperm to travel to the uterus. Afterwards, the cervix closes and the uterus lowers itself on top of the vagina.

Changes specific to the man's body during the resolution stage:
- The penis becomes flaccid.
- The scrotum lowers pulling the testes away from the body.

The Sexual Response Cycle in Men following a Spinal Cord Injury

During the **excitement stage** men with spinal cord injuries, especially those with upper level injuries are unable to obtain a psychogenic erection. This is due to an interruption or break in the pathway between the brain and the hypogastic plexus located between T11 and L2. However, those individuals with upper level injuries are able to obtain reflex erections caused by afferent and efferent impulses going to and from the sacral spinal cord located between S2 and S4. This will be discussed in greater detail in Chapter 4. During the **orgasm stage** many men with an SCI have reported the inability to have an ejaculation. A study of 408 men with SCI above T12 found that 75% of the men reported being able to achieve an erection, whereas, only 10% reported having experienced an ejaculation (Linsenmeyer, 2000). This will be discussed further in Chapter 5.

Erogenous Zones

Erogenous zones are areas of the body that are sensitive to touch because of a high concentration of sensory nerves located in and around these areas. During times of sexual excitement, stimulation of these areas by touch increases the level of sexual arousal. To be an effective lover, you must know what is sexually pleasing to your partner. It is important that you try to discover everything you can about your partner's body. What areas of his/her body are the most sensitive to touch? You may need to experiment with various types of touch, strokes, or kisses to find what excites your partner. Begin by using your hands and your fingers to touch your partner's body. Allow your partner to use his/her feet to rub or stroke your body. Try using your mouth, lips, and tongue to stimulate your partner's body. The glans of the penis can by used to rub or stroke your partner's body. A woman can use her breasts and nipples to sexually stimulate her male partner. It is important that you and your partner provide each other with immediate feedback as to what you like and what feels good. The secret is to start slowly and to openly communicate with your partner. It is important to keep in mind that erogenous zones vary from person to person.

The Man's Erogenous Zones. The general erogenous zones of a man's body would include his lips, face, chest, back, and nipples. The main erogenous zone of a man is the penis, which is very sensitive to touch, temperature, and pressure because of the many sensory nerves in the area of the glans and shaft. The frenulum is an extremely sensitive area of the penis when stimulated. The scrotum is another area that, when touched and stroked, brings great pleasure. However, the scrotum is very sensitive to pressure. A tight grip of the scrotum can be rather painful. The area located between the penis and anus is an erogenous zone that is sensitive to the touch. The anus, because of the many nerve endings is an extremely sensitive area. Many men have noted that having a finger inserted into the anus as they near orgasm tends to heighten the sensation of the orgasm. The buttocks is also very sensitive to physical stimulation and can increase sexual pleasure if stroked, rubbed, or playfully slapped during the excitement stage of the sexual response cycle.

The man's erogenous zones following a spinal cord injury (SCI) will vary depending on the level of injury and the extent of the paralysis. In many cases areas above the level of injury will become hypersensitive to touch and physical stimulation. Many men with an SCI find that physical stimulation to this area is a source of great erotic pleasure and extremely sexually arousing. However, other men with SCIs find that stimulation of these areas is rather painful and not a pleasurable experience. Men with an SCI have reported that areas of their body that were not sensitive prior to the injury have become sensitive to physical touch. Several erogenous zones for a C5 quadriplegic might include the nipple line, the neck, the earlobes, the upper chest, and shoulders. Some quadriplegics have reported that a high level of stimulation to these areas have resulted in fantasy orgasms.

The Woman's Erogenous Zones. A woman's erogenous zones will vary from woman to woman. This is why it is important to get to know your partner's body. A woman's body has several erogenous zones. A major erogenous zone of a woman is her skin, which includes her entire body. Try rubbing her arms, legs, back, stomach, feet, or thighs to discover which areas of her skin are more sensitive than others.

A woman's face also has several erogenous zones including her forehead, hairline, eyelids, eyebrows, cheeks, and lips. Try using your hand and fingertips to lightly stroke and touch these areas while noting her reactions. The area of the neck may be another erogenous area that is very sensitive to touching and kissing. The back and sides of the neck may be especially sensitive to touch. The earlobes can be another extremely sensitive area of a woman when stimulated by touching or kissing. Just be aware of the possibility of some very strong reactions when kissing your partner's earlobes. Many women find that physical stimulation to this area is a source of great erotic pleasure which in some women can actually result in an orgasm. However, other women find that stimulation to the earlobes is rather painful and not a pleasurable experience. Listen and observe how your partner is responding.

Still another major erogenous zone of a woman is her mouth. Because of a high concentration of sensory nerves, the mouth is a very sensitive area of the body. You can explore your partner's mouth by using your fingertips, your lips, and your tongue. Try light kissing using your lips. Lead up to gentle strokes with your tongue as you explore your partner's lips and the inside of her mouth.
As a woman becomes sexually aroused, her breasts will increase in sensitivity. Many women find it highly erotic to have their breasts touched, caressed, and kissed. As you rub over her breasts, the nipples will become erect, and the breasts may slightly increase in size as her level of arousal increases.

Other areas which are considered erogenous zones would include her navel and legs. A woman's navel and the area surrounding the navel can be sensitive to light touching and kissing. A woman's legs, especially her inner thighs, are highly sensitive areas to touching and kissing.

For women the most sensitive erogenous zone is their vulva, especially the clitoris. Other sensitive areas would include the labia majora and minora, the opening of the vagina, and the perineum. For some the anus is another extremely sensitive area leading to a heightened state of arousal when stimulated. As a woman nears orgasm, inserting a finger into the opening of the anus may be extremely pleasurable and intensify the sexual experience. In addition, a woman's buttock is an erogenous zone that should not be neglected. Some women enjoy having their buttocks stroked, rubbed, or lightly slapped as they become sexually aroused. The important thing is to listen and observe as to how your partner responds to your touch.

Congratulations!! You have just completed a basic course on sexual and spinal anatomy. We will now begin to explore sexuality as it is related to having a spinal cord injury.

Suggested Readings and Resources

Berger, F. G. (1988). _The G-Spot in Words and Pictures_. Flensburg: Orion.

Miriam, S. (1991). _The Magic of Sex_. New York: DK Publishing.

Moglis, R. F., & Knowles, J. (1997). _All About Sex: A Family Resource on Sex and Sexuality_. New York: Three Rivers Press.

Chapter 3
Communicating, Dating,
& Relationships

Our society has a rather negative stereotype of individuals with disabilities in regard to the issue of sexuality. In the not so distant past the topic of sexuality and disabilities was avoided or ignored. As a result, myths and stereotypes emerged which greatly affected how the non-disabled population treated and interacted with individuals with disabilities. In addition, these myths and stereotypes have prevented many individuals with spinal cord injuries from experiencing freedom of sexual expression. Consequently, people with disabilities have often been unable to develop positive images of themselves as sexually attractive human beings. In response to this apparent negative attitude, George Washington University conducted a study known as the "Sex and Disability Project." The purpose of the project was to identify those myths and stereotypes commonly associated with sexuality and disability. The study found the following common stereotypes:

- Individuals with disabilities are asexual.
- Individuals with disabilities breed others with disabilities.
- Individuals with disabilities are oversexed and have uncontrollable urges.
- Individuals with disabilities should only marry others with similar disabilities.
- Parents with a disabled child do not want that child educated about his/her sexuality.
- In order to be satisfying, sexual intercourse must end in an orgasm.
- If an individual with a disability has a sexual problem, it is the result of his/her disability.
- If a non-disabled individual becomes sexually involved with a disabled individual it is because they cannot attract anyone else (Chipouras et al., 1979).

Each of these myths and stereotypes were an attempt to prove that individuals with disabilities were undesirable and inferior as sexual beings when compared to non-disabled individuals. A woman with an SCI, who participated in a recent study on self-development and attitude towards sexuality in individuals with disabilities and the attitude of the American culture, stated that for a period of time she had been considered a "slut" because of being sexually active. In a sense she considered being called a slut a "badge of honor" because to her it meant she was challenging the myths and stereotypes that suggest that because she has a disability she is not to be sexually active or considered desirable as a sexual partner. Even her parents reinforced these myths by telling her that "someday a man would love her enough to sleep with her despite her disability" (Guldin, 2000). Instead of helping her explore and develop her sexuality, she was shamed and discouraged by others, including her parents, which reinforced these myths and stereotypes. However, attitudes are changing. We now know that having a spinal cord injury does not alter one's sexuality or one's desire to have sex. In fact, following a spinal cord injury, some of the most frequently asked questions are about sexuality and the individual's ability to perform sexually.

In the past, once someone had sustained a spinal cord injury, most of the focus during the rehabilitation process was on improving the patient's physical health and strength, and teaching them daily living skills. Teaching a patient how to socialize and interact with others following a spinal cord injury was often left up to the individual once he/she left the rehabilitation center. However, this is changing as more and more rehabilitation programs are including education about sexuality as part of the rehabilitation process.

Living your life with a spinal cord injury is not a curse unless you make it one. There are many individuals with spinal cord injuries who are involved in successful relationships. These individuals actively socialize with others, date, marry, and raise a family just like any "normal" non-spinal cord injured man would do. Many individuals with SCIs who are involved in successful relationships probably at one point experienced many of the same fears you may be having now about becoming involved in a relationship. However, what most of these individuals have in common that helped them overcome their fears is a high level of positive self-esteem, a positive self-image, a feeling of self-worth, and a desire to share their lives with someone they love. If you have a spinal cord injury, this chapter will explore several fears that you may face when you first desire to become romantically and sexually involved in a relationship. We will look at ways of making you feel comfortable and will give you suggestions about how to talk to a woman about your injury. We will also teach you how to improve your communication skills, how to express your needs, how to improve your chances of dating, and how to deal with issues that can occur when you least expect them. It is important to keep in mind that first impressions do count. If you have the right attitude, a sense of humor, and the ability to make others feel comfortable around you, then a potential partner will easily see past your wheelchair and your disability and focus on you.

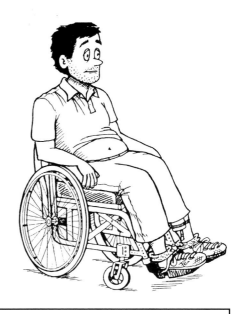

Figure 3.1 How not to look when you're going out with others.

Personal Care and Appearance

Our society tends to place a lot of emphasis on physical appearance. Improving the way you look can not only attract others to you but can also improve how you feel about yourself. Let's begin with the basics.

Personal hygiene is very important, especially if you want others to enjoy being in your presence. Bathing daily or every other day helps to control body odor. This also helps maintain healthy skin, which can prevent pressure sores and infections. Good grooming habits are also important. Comb your hair daily or before going out to meet with others. Shaving daily or maintaining your facial hair can help you improve your physical appearance. Most importantly, don't forget to brush your teeth and use mouthwash. There is nothing worse than trying to converse with someone who has bad breath. If you have a problem with persistent bad breath, consult your dentist or physician. In addition, particular attention should be paid to the management and care of your appliances including catheters, leg bags, and seat cushions. No one wants to smell foul urine from an old unclean leg bag that should have been discarded three months ago. Don't forget to wash the cover or wipe off your seat cushion at least once a week. Odors from passing gas often tend to get trapped and linger in one's seat cushion. Trust me no one wants to smell "butt rounch" when you transfer out of your wheelchair. It tends to spoil the mood. Be conscious of your odors so that you do not offend others.

The way you dress and how you present yourself to others can also affect how others are attracted to you. A good rule to remember is to select clothing that makes you look good and is easy to manage. Choose a style that enhances your best features and minimizes attention to any differences in your appearance. Wearing shorts or pants that expose your leg bag half filled with urine, wearing pants that do not rise above your hips so that your "butt crack" is exposed or wearing a tight shirt that exposes your quad belly are not likely to help with that first impression (see Figure 3.1). In addition, dressing in only one type of clothes such as sweatpants or T-shirts may limit the type of places others are willing to go with you in public. Companies like USA Jeans specialize in making clothing such as jeans and dress pants designed especially for individuals in wheelchairs. These clothes can be ordered in various colors and material thicknesses, and they come with several options making them easier to put on and remove. No pockets on the seat of the pants create a reduced risk for pressure sores, and extra room in the legs accommodate the expansion of leg bags or the use of braces. These clothes are tailored to fit your body, which makes you feel and look comfortable in the clothing you are wearing. Being able to feel good about your appearance can not only improve your self-esteem, but it can also enhance how you feel about yourself as a potential sexual partner.

The color of your wheelchair can also be a way in which you express your personal style to others. Some individuals like things that are hot, bright, and flashy, so they choose bright vivid colors such as red, hot pink, blue, or purple for the frame of their wheelchair. Others prefer the shiny chrome and steel look. However, if you want people to focus their attention more on you and less on your wheelchair, consider a color such as black or dark gray. A black wheelchair is especially useful in professional relationships.

Body Image

Body image refers to the attitude and feeling we each have about our own body. Our society tends to place a lot of emphasis on body image. We are conditioned to believe that women desire only men who are strong and masculine. As a result, many adolescent boys and men spend a lot of time in the local gym or health club trying to improve their body image by exercising and lifting weights. But having a spinal cord injury resulting in the loss of body functions such as the inability to walk, loss of feeling and muscle strength, the inability to use arms or hands, or the development of a quad belly can all affect one's body image. Likewise, items such as wheelchairs, braces, catheters, leg bags, and bowel programs can also have an impact on one's self-image. The importance placed on one's body image or athletic ability prior to becoming injured can greatly affect one's ability to adjust to his body image following an injury. In order to have a positive adjustment following an SCI, one must be willing to recognize his body's abilities as well as it's limitations. Individuals are often affected by what is known as the "imaginary audience." This means that the individual feels that everyone around them is watching and knows all their secrets. They feel there is a billboard somewhere that reveals all of their embarrassing moments. Depending on the level of injury, it may be possible to maintain a body in good shape by performing daily exercises, lifting weights, or doing other types of physical activities. Individuals who are sports oriented may become involved in wheelchair sports and can compete in such sports as basketball, tennis, track and field, swimming, quad rugby, and various others. Participating in wheelchair sports is an excellent way to meet individuals who have successfully adjusted to their spinal cord injuries and other non-disabled individuals who share the same interests. For individuals not into sports daily exercise and eating healthy can help to control weight gain.

Emotions

One of the more difficult tasks for an individual following a spinal cord injury is to take control of his emotions. It is very easy to become overwhelmed by the flood of anger, fears, and frustrations one experiences after an injury. Many individuals with an SCI progress through an emotional adjustment period. This adjustment period is similar to the stage theory of death (grief) proposed by Elisabeth Kubler Ross. According to Kubler Ross, a person progresses through five stages of grief when faced with a death or a loss: denial, anger, bargaining, depression, and acceptance. Not everyone progresses through each of these stages nor is there a set time limit as to how long one remains in each stage. However, in order for a person to successfully cope, he must achieve the final stage of acceptance (Johnson, 1993). Individuals who suffer a traumatic experience such as an SCI also progress through these same stages.

The first steps in allowing others to like you and feel comfortable being with you is to develop a positive attitude and to like yourself. Having a spinal cord injury doesn't change the person inside. It is important for you to understand that you have the conscious ability to choose how you want to react to others. Because we have the ability to think, respond, and act, we have the ability to control how we feel and how we relate to others. You can choose to be angry and bitter at the world, blaming everyone for your misfortunes, or you can accept things as they are, develop a positive attitude, and decide to make the best of your life. Just remember that God never gave anyone a guarantee that life was going to be fair or without struggle. At one point in my own recovery, I came to the realization that I had a choice to make. I could sit in my wheelchair, be bitter towards others, and feel sorry about my losses, or I could accept what I had and live each day of my life to it fullest. I chose the latter. Unfortunately, there is no way of stopping time. Each individual with an SCI must choose to either watch time pass by or decide to become an active participant. Life is a journey from the day we are born until the day we die. We must choose how much we want to be involved and whether or not we want to enjoy the trip. Research studies have proven that individuals with spinal cord injuries who believe they have internal control of their destiny were more likely to take care of themselves, pursue educational opportunities, seek employment opportunities, and were found to have an overall greater satisfaction with life (Swenson, 1978). The more we feel we have control over our lives, the higher our level of positive adjustment. In general it is important to remember that people tend to enjoy being around others who have a positive outlook on life and are pleasant to be around. If you want to date and become involved in a relationship, you need to become an active participant in life. Very few individuals with an SCI have ever met someone by just staying at home and refusing to go out. If you have a negative attitude or have been unable to shake away the blues, you must seek the services of a psychologist or professional counselor. Some individuals who become severely depressed following their SCI may need medication to help them overcome the symptoms of depression. If you feel the need for an attitude adjustment, take a step in a positive direction and seek the help you need.

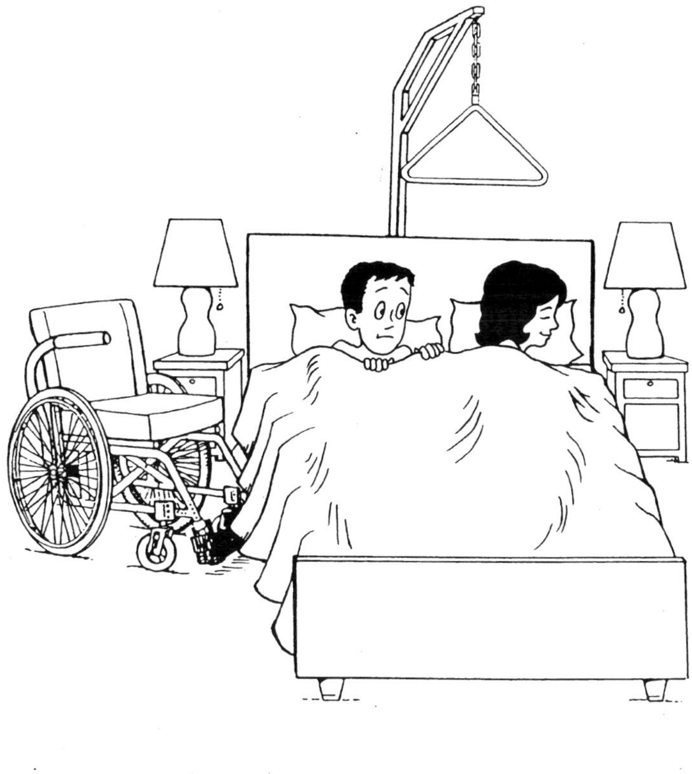

Figure 3.2 When roles are reversed - Well now that she is satisfied what about me??

Sexual Satisfaction Following an SCI

The truth about sexual satisfaction following an SCI depends on a number of factors. These factors would include your age, whether or not you had been sexually active prior to your injury, your level of physical sensation, your ability to have an orgasm, and your sex drive, just to name a few. If prior to your injury you had never experienced sexual intercourse with a woman, it would be impossible to compare it with having sexual intercourse after an SCI. However, if prior to your injury you had sexual intercourse with a woman, then you may notice a difference. Even if you had never experienced an orgasm during sexual intercourse with a woman but had an orgasm as a result of masturbating then you are aware of the great feeling of relief and calmness following the orgasm. It is this feeling that is often lost as the result of a spinal cord injury. The loss of this feeling is what often leads to sexual frustration in men with SCIs. We have all heard women say once their man has had his orgasm, he rolls over in bed and falls asleep leaving her sexually frustrated because she did not have her orgasm. It seems that there is a role reversal when it comes to relationships between men with SCIs and their female partners (see Figure 3.2). In these cases the woman has the orgasm then rolls over and falls asleep, and the guy is still waiting for his orgasm to occur. This may be one reason why men with SCIs become preoccupied with sex. When there is no release for this sexual tension, the tension begins to grow causing the individual to become sexually frustrated. Some individuals with an SCI have reported experiencing physical orgasms in their shoulders or their lips. Others have reported having more abstract orgasms such as mental orgasms, heart orgasms, and full body inspiring orgasms (Guldin, 2000). In my personal experience, however, I have never had such orgasms even though I have been very sexually active since my injury.

Therefore, in order to develop a pleasurable sex life, men with an SCI must be willing to adjust their expectations of the sexual experience. In other words, they must be willing to make a mental switch. Many individuals discover that they experience great pleasure in making love to their partners and giving them the best orgasm they can. Their pleasure comes from knowing that they can love their partner the way they want to be loved. It doesn't matter whether the orgasm experienced is physical or abstract. What is important is that you are able to redefine how you interpret or experience an orgasm in light of your body's new level of functioning and sensation.

Bowel and Bladder Issues

A fear that most men with an SCI have when it comes to dating or having a sexual encounter is the fear of having a bowel or bladder accident. In fact, some men have even avoided becoming involved in a relationship because of this fear. With the loss of control over bowel and bladder functioning as a result of the spinal cord injury, there is always the possibility that an accident could happen. What is important is how you deal with the situation. Having a bowel or bladder accident is part of a spinal injury that you need to accept. Having or developing a sense of humor helps in situations when an accident does occur. And for the most part it always seems that a bowel or bladder accident occurs at the wrong time, not that there is ever a right time.

I remember my first semester in college sitting in the lobby of my dorm talking to several beautiful girls when one of them informed me that I was urinating on the floor. Sure enough, there was a rather large puddle of urine forming on the white tile floor under my wheelchair. Apparently my personal care attendant had forgotten to close the clamp to my leg bag. Talk about an embarrassing moment! My first response was, "Now who would pee on the floor under my chair?" I just wanted to die. I'm thinking to myself, "Now what do I do?" Believe it or not, the girl who noticed quickly closed the clamp and helped to mop up the floor. We ended up becoming good friends and dated for several semesters. There have been numerous occasions when I have been in the process of having sexual intercourse or in the process of performing oral sex where the weight or the thrusting of my partner's body on my stomach triggered my bladder causing us to stop our sexual activity until after my bladder emptied. The best way to deal with these situations is to grab the urinal, allow your bladder to empty, clean yourself, and return to what you had been doing.

Bowel accidents can also occur, especially if you are overly stressed or if you eat something that doesn't agree with your digestive system. It is important to be aware of what foods cause you to have bowel problems and avoid them while on dates. An example would be foods such as sauerkraut, hot peppers, or onion soup. If stress seems to be the problem it might be beneficial for you to learn relaxation and other stress reducing techniques such as thought stopping. If stress is an ongoing problem you may need to seek the services of a psychologist or counselor.

The best advice in dealing with bowel and bladder issues is to take preventive steps. Begin by maintaining a regular bowel and bladder program; this can help to prevent accidents. Talk to your partner about the possibility of having a bowel or bladder accident. Explain to her what she can do to assist you should an accident occur. A woman who cares about you and wants a relationship with you will have no problem helping you. She may seem uncomfortable at first because this may be a new situation for her, but stay calm, don't become frustrated, and talk her through the situation.

Sexual activity and/or stimulation of the genitals could also cause a bowel or bladder accident. If having an accident is a concern for you, the risk can be greatly reduced if you empty your bowel and bladder prior to having sex. Having sex does not mean an accident will occur. However, be aware that an accident is more likely to occur if your bowel and bladder are full. In any event, it would be wise for you to keep a urinal and some towels next to the bed just in case you need them. If you feel your bladder trigger while in the process of having sex, take a break and have your partner assist you the best that she can. When you have finished and have cleaned yourself up, return to the action. The important thing is to remain calm and relaxed. Once again, having a sense of humor can greatly assist you in dealing with these types of situations; it will make the moment seem less embarrassing and can help both you and your partner adjust to it. If you accept yourself and listen to what your body tells you, then you are far less likely to have problems. If you make things seem as if they are routine, then your partner will think everything is normal. It is very important to be comfortable with yourself and openly communicate with your partner. Bowel and bladder accidents will occur; it is just a fact of life with having a spinal cord injury. Being aware of what causes accidents and avoiding these triggers will reduce the risk of an accident regardless if you and your partner are out on a date or engaged in a sexual encounter.

Personal Care Issues

A concern that many men with SCIs have upon discharge from the rehabilitation center is personal care. This is especially true for individuals with higher level injuries who need to rely on others to do the majority of their personal care including a bowel and bladder program, dressing, bathing, and assistance with eating. While in the hospital and rehabilitation center these tasks are performed by a qualified and trained nursing staff or nurse's aides. However, once the individual is discharged from the hospital, the task of caregiver usually becomes the sole responsibility of a family member. Some communities have personal care attendants or visiting nurses who will come on a daily basis to perform the necessary personal care. If you are interested in knowing if your community offers personal care assistance, contact your rehabilitation center, the local health and welfare office, the local state office for vocational rehabilitation, or your local center for independent living.

A thought that often preoccupies the minds of men with an SCI following their injury is "Will I ever find someone who will want to be in a relationship with me after she realizes how much work and time will be required to take care of me?" You must realize that a woman who wants to be with you in a relationship will accept you _and_ your personal care needs. You need to become comfortable with others doing your personal care. I remember the fear that I had the first time a young woman my age did this for me. It was just my second day of my freshman year at Edinboro University of Pennsylvania. A young attractive nursing student named Fran came cheerfully waltzing into my room to inform me that she was ready to start my bowel program. One of the first things I asked Fran was her age. I was shocked to discover that we were the same age. Up to that point I had never even thought about a woman my own age doing my personal care, especially a young attractive woman. My perspective changed as the weeks went by and other young female attendants took their turns helping me. The important thing for you to do is to discuss this issue with your partner and not try to read her mind. Ask her how she feels about your personal care. Begin slowly to ease her into what is involved in taking care of you. Having her help you take your coat on and off, cutting your food at a restaurant, emptying your leg bag, helping with transfers to or from a car are all small things to help her understand the assistance you need. As she becomes more aware of your personal needs, she can become more involved with your personal care. It is very important to communicate with each other. Don't make the mistake of deserting your partner because you think she will be better off without you. Allow your partner to make that choice. I almost made this mistake. When I was dating my wife in college, I was in graduate school, and she was in her junior year. When I knew I was leaving school to move back home with my parents to do my internship, I started to push her away from me. I felt she could have a better life by dating and falling in love with an able-bodied man, so I did the worst thing I could have done. I tried to shut her out of my life. I could not understand why she would want to have a relationship with me. What I failed to do was to ask her how she felt. I tried to make the decision for her, but she made it very clear that I had no right to make that choice for her. She wanted to be with me, and she told me that she realized that being with me included taking care of my needs. She accepted that as a part of our relationship. Ten years later we are still going strong.

Therefore, once you are involved in a relationship, it is important to discuss with your partner to what degree (if any) she will be responsible for your personal care. She may prefer to do all of your personal care, or depending on other factors such as raising children or having a career of her own, she may prefer hiring visiting nurses or personal care attendants to perform some or all of your daily personal care needs. The important thing is to talk about it and be sure that you are both comfortable with the choices made.

Dating and Beginning Relationships

As I have stated earlier if you want to date and become involved in a relationship, you must become an active member in society. Fearing to go out in public or staying at home surrounded by four walls is not going to help you meet potential dating partners. If you are uncomfortable about going out in public, start slowly with the company of a few close friends and gradually increase the time you spend out with others (see Figure 3.3). If your friends ask you to go out with them don't turn down the offer. If you want to meet others, you must be willing to go where people gather such as church, school, or work. Consider becoming involved in community groups and organizations. Some individuals have met people through internet dating services or by being involved in a "chat room." You could also try a local dating service. If you are a young male with an SCI, you should seriously consider attending a full-time college that is totally wheelchair accessible, offers accessible housing, and 24-hour attendant care. Going to college can not only help you prepare for a career, but college life also provides you with many opportunities for socializing with peers your own age. A friend of mine called college "a target rich environment" for meeting young women. He was very right. In fact, I met my beautiful wife in college.

When you first begin dating, it is imperative for you and your partner to be honest and to have open communication. Remember, it is your responsibility to educate your lover about your sexual abilities, physical limitations, desires, and fears. You must also allow your partner to discuss her needs and her fears. In some ways this communication can be used as a form of verbal foreplay as you each describe your likes and desires.

For those of you who were married at the time of your injury, there will be an adjustment period that your spouse will go through. Some of this adjustment will have to include a change in roles and assigned tasks. These may include the housework, the yard work, taking out the trash, watching and caring for the children, and so on. If you brought in the majority of the family's income prior to your injury and are unable to return to that type of work, the loss of income can have a major impact on the family causing enormous stress. The adjustment period of a spinal cord injury can be a very stressful time in many relationships. Some couples are able to make the necessary changes, whereas other relationships will end. If your relationship begins to suffer as a result of the injury, it is highly recommended that you seek the assistance of a marriage and family therapist. As always it is important to have open and honest communication between you and your partner. If your relationship ends for

Figure 3.3 Romantic Dinner for Two.

whatever reason, give your heart and mind some time to heal. Then the best thing you can do is to pick yourself up, dust yourself off, and seek comfort through old friends or try making some new ones. In time you may decide to become involved in another relationship. The choice is yours. If depression or anger becomes a problem, seek professional help.

Chapter 4
Erectile Dysfunction
and Treatment

The National Institute of Health Consensus Panel has defined erectile dysfunction as the inability to achieve or maintain an erection sufficient for satisfactory sexual performance (Maytom, Derry, Dinsmore, Glass, Smith, Orr, & Osterloh, 1999). Erectile dysfunction is one of the major sexual complications faced by men who have experienced a spinal cord injury (SCI). Generally speaking, most men with spinal cord injuries, regardless of where the lesion has occurred, will experience some degree of erectile dysfunction. Under normal circumstances the ability to achieve an erection is controlled by the parasympathetic nervous system. When sexual excitement or stimulation of the penis occurs, the parasympathetic nervous system sends a message to the blood vessels in the penis allowing blood to enter the corpora cavernosa and the corpus spongiosum, causing an erection. The inability to achieve an erection following a spinal cord injury is the result of a disruption of this message somewhere along the spinal pathway between the brain and the penis. As a result, the penis is unable to respond to sexual stimuli as it did prior to the injury. When it comes to being able to obtain an erection, human males are unique from other mammals. They have the ability to obtain an erection through psychic stimulation as a result of sexual thoughts, visual images, or sexual touching. However, a man with a spinal cord injury may not be able to experience a psychological erection, even though his body may become sexually aroused resulting in increased breathing, faster heart rate, and sex flush. The penis no longer responds to sexual stimuli. The erotic stimulation of watching an x-rated video or looking at nude photos, which previously produced an erection, will no longer cause one to occur. The degree of erectile dysfunction in men with an SCI varies according to several factors. These include the level of injury, whether the injury is complete or incomplete, what medications are being taken, the individual's current psychological state of mind, and the individual's age.

At this point some of you might be saying to yourself, "But I'm a male with a spinal cord injury, and I still have erections." This fact is true for many men with an SCI. However, there are two types of erections: a psychogenic erection and a reflexogenic erection. Psychogenic erections occur when a signal is sent from the brain to the penis resulting in an erection. This erection is the result of either physical or psychological stimulation or a combination of the two. As stated above, a psychogenic erection occurs when a man becomes sexually stimulated by observing a naked woman, while looking at nude photos, or while having sexual fantasies about a woman who is sitting next to him, etc.

A reflexogenic erection occurs as the result of physical touch or muscle spasms in the groin area. The brain does not control this type of an erection. The erection is the result of afferent and efferent impulses going to and from the sacral spinal cord. There is no relationship between a reflexogenic erection and one's level of sexual excitement. This type of erection can often occur while the nurse, personal care attendant, or your partner puts an external catheter on your penis. Many quadriplegics are able to obtain reflexogenic erections. However, there are two problems usually associated with a reflexogenic erection and having sex with a partner: first, a reflexogenic erection usually is not hard enough to allow for vaginal penetration, and second, individuals who are able to achieve reflexogenic erections often are unable to maintain the erection long enough to allow for successful sexual intercourse. A study conducted on 115 men with SCIs found that 92% where able to obtain an erection. However, because of the poor quality of the erection obtained only 44% of the men with complete injuries and 56% of the men with incomplete injuries where successful at having intercourse (Linsenmeyer, 2000). Although, it is interesting to note that many male quadriplegics with incomplete injuries have reported being successful in having vaginal intercourse with reflexogenic erections. This will be discussed further under "stuffing." Studies have shown that reflexogenic erections occur more frequently in men with higher-level spinal cord injuries as compared to men with lower level spinal cord injuries, T9 through S5. The reason lower lesion paraplegic men are unable to have an erection is that the spinal nerves which cause reflexogenic erections do not function at lower level injuries. Some researchers have discovered that reflexogenic erections occurred 50% of the time in SCI patients with sacral cord lesions as compared to 93% in SCI patients with cervical injuries (Lizza, 1990).

Even though at this point in your reading you may feel as if the odds are stacked against you regarding your ability to obtain an erection suitable for sexual pleasure, there is light at the end of the tunnel. The important question that you must answer is, "What is my goal?" If your goal is to have an erection that results in an orgasm and an ejaculation, the possibilities of this occurring are slim. If this is a major concern for you, it is highly recommended that you speak to your physician or a psychologist. On the other hand, if your goal is to achieve an erection allowing you to have vaginal penetration for sexual pleasure, then you have some options. There are several techniques a man with a spinal cord injury can use to assist him in obtaining an erection. The choice depends on several factors including cost, the level of the injury, the amount of sensation and feeling the individual has in his penis, and whether or not he can achieve a reflexogenic erection. The remainder of this chapter will elaborate on the treatment options for erectile dysfunction. We will begin by discussing techniques which are the most natural and least expensive and progress through techniques that require surgery, can be rather expensive, and can result in some physical and emotional complications. Most individuals, in trying to determine what technique works best for them, should try experimenting with several methods beginning with the least invasive and/or consulting with a physician.

Treatments for Erectile Dysfunction

Stuffing: Stuffing is the most natural and least expensive of the techniques to obtain an erection. This technique works best with those individuals who retain the ability to have reflexogenic erections. Stuffing involves the woman inserting the flaccid penis into her vagina (see Figure 4.1). A reflexogenic erection occurs as a result of the physical touch and stimulation when the penis is inserted into the vagina. Some men have discovered that physical stimulation to their genitals and the area surrounding their genitals can cause a reflexogenic erection. Others have discovered that their spasms, especially in their legs and inner thighs, can cause a reflexogenic erection. If you are an individual whose leg spasms often cause you to have erections, why not take advantage of the situation and use these spasms in your favor? In order to maintain the erection, your partner can voluntarily contract the muscles of her vagina to grip your penis.

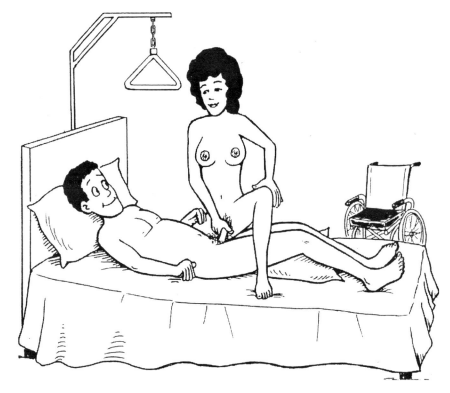

Figure 4.1 Stuffing

33

The desired result is that the erection becomes hard enough to allow you and your partner to have vaginal intercourse. The disadvantage of the stuffing technique is that you have no control over the amount of time that your penis will maintain the erection. Usually once the physical sensation discontinues, so does the erection, and the penis returns to the flaccid state. If you and your partner are interested in using the stuffing technique, take time to learn about your body. Note what types of physical stimulation cause you to have an erection.

Non-Invasive Aids: If you have the ability to have a reflexogenic erection suitable for having sexual intercourse but have difficulty maintaining the erection, there are several options you can use to maintain the erection. A thick rubber band doubled up or a cock ring (see Chapter 8) can be placed at the base of the penis to help maintain the erection. Another option is to use the StayErec™ System from Osbon Medical System. The StayErec™ System uses tension rings to maintain an erection (see Photo 4.1). You can choose a ring of various tensions or use a combination of rings in order to maintain an erection. The StayErec™ System easily allows you to slide the tension ring onto the base of the penis once you have achieved maximum erection.

Photo 4.1 A Tension Ring

WARNING: Regardless if you use the rubber band, cock ring, or tension ring, it **must be removed** from the penis when or before 30 minutes has elapsed in order to prevent any skin breakdowns or other medical problems. Once the band or ring is removed, the penis will return to its flaccid state.

Penile Vacuum Pumps: Penile vacuum pumps have become a very popular method used by men with an SCI and by able-bodied men who suffer from erectile dysfunction. The success rate of this form of treatment is 90%. The original vacuum pump was the ErecAid System developed in the early 1960s by Gedding Osbon. Penile vacuum pumps such as the ErecAid System (now known as the Esteem produced by Endocare, Inc.) have many positive features including the following:

- The technique has been proven to be safe.
- Using the pump provides immediate results.
- There are no drugs or injections involved.
- The technique requires no surgery.
- There are no serious side effects from using this technique.
- Using the pump to create the erection is an easy technique for you or your partner to perform.

The vacuum pump uses the principle of negative pressure to create a naturally engorged erection. The penis is first lubricated and inserted into the clear plastic cylinder. Lubricating the penis helps create a seal for maintaining the vacuum. It may also be helpful to lubricate the inside of the cylinder to prevent any friction the penis may experience as it expands within the cylinder. Once the penis is inserted, the cylinder is held firmly against the body. The pump, depending on the type purchased, is used by squeezing the hand pump or activating the battery operated pump, which creates a vacuum inside the cylinder (see Photo 4.3). Once an erection is obtained the tension ring, which is placed around the cylinder prior to inserting the penis, is transferred from the cylinder to the base of the penis. This ring maintains the erection once the vacuum is released. The penis should be firm enough to allow for intercourse with your partner. However, as stated earlier the tension ring **must be removed** from the penis at or before 30 minutes to prevent any medical problems. Once the tension ring is removed, the penis will return to the flaccid state.

There are several things that you need to be aware of when using this devise. Using a vacuum devise will cause the circumference of the penis to increase in size. Also, the tension ring may cause the penis to turn a dark purplish color and feel cold to the touch. This is a normal occurrence. Once the tension ring is removed, the penis will return to normal flesh color and body temperature. Again, it is very important to remember to leave the tension rings on the penis no longer than 30 minutes.

Photo 4.2 Penile Vacuum Device

Failure to remove the tension rings will cause prolonged compression at the base of the penis. This could result in a condition known as tissue necrosis. There have been only two reports of minor side effects caused by the use of a vacuum devise: petechiae and ecchymosis. Petechiae are reddish pinpoint spots on the penis that occur when the penis has not been properly conditioned to the rapid negative pressure caused by the vacuum. The other condition, ecchymosis, is bruising of the penis resulting from over exposure to the pressure of the vacuum. Neither of these conditions are life threatening and can easily be prevented by following the manufacturer's directions for use. The main complaint from couples using a penile vacuum devise is that the process of using the devise does not feel natural. One way to solve this problem is to use the devise during foreplay. Having your partner "pump you up" can be rather arousing. Overall, the penile vacuum devise has been found to be a safe and effective method for obtaining an erection. The majority of the men and their partners who use the vacuum devises are satisfied. This particular vacuum pump can be rather costly; however, most insurance companies will reimburse the purchase of this and some similar devices. The manufacturer as well as the insurance company will require a prescription from your physician for the purchase of the vacuum devise.

Helpful Hint: If you have a lot of pubic hair around the base of your penis you may want to consider trimming the hair. This will prevent the hair from being pulled into the cylinder or from getting caught in the tension rings.

Penile Injections: This technique involves using a small needle to inject a medication into the corpus cavernosa. This causes the smooth muscles of the penis to become relaxed thus allowing blood to flow into the penis resulting in an erection. In July of 1996, the FDA approved Alprostadil (Caverjet) as the first penile injection drug to be used for the treatment of erectile dysfunction (Ducharme, 1997). This drug is widely used today, and the reported success rate is 84% (Mark & Light, 1990).

There are several potential complications with using penile injections. Individuals with any sensation in the penis may experience pain from the initial and repeated insertion of a needle. In addition, multiple injections can cause scarring and bruising of the penis. Because this technique involves the use of needles, bleeding may occur. Therefore, one must be aware of the increased risk of contracting HIV and AIDS when using this technique. If the threat of HIV/AIDS is a concern, it is best to avoid those individuals who are in a high-risk population. These individuals include those who practice unsafe sex, have multiple sex partners, or are intravenous drug users who share needles. Another possible complication with using this technique is a condition known as *priapism*, a prolonged erection caused by the individual exceeding the recommended dosage requiring immediate medical treatment.

Penile Implants: Penile implants have traditionally been used as the main form of treatment for erectile dysfunction in men with spinal cord injuries. The first attempts at using penile implants date back to 1937 when rib cartilage was surgically implanted into the penis. There were two major complications with this early penile prosthesis. After a period of time the cartilage would begin to curl or it would be reabsorbed by the body (Auerbach, 1982). Since the late 1930s there have been vast improvements in penile implants.

In the 1960s a rigid silicon rod was developed which was surgically implanted in the shaft of the penis. The main problem with this penile implant was that it could become dislodged from its original placement causing discomfort (Linsenmeyer, 1991). To solve this problem, they began to surgically place two rigid rods into each of the corpus cavernosa, the soft spongy tissue located on each side of the shaft of the penis. One of the main complaints about the rigid penile implants was that of cosmetic concealment. This became a source of embarrassment to some individuals. The penis, because it maintained a constant state of erection, would often protrude outward making it visible through clothing. Recently, newer models have been developed taking into account the patient's outward appearance, comfort, and emotional concerns regarding the penile implant. Currently there are two types of penile implants: the semi-rigid penile implant and the inflatable penile prosthesis.

The semirigid penile implant was first developed in 1975 (Linsenmeyer, 1991). These penile implants were made to be flexible to better meet the need for concealment. The Dura-II™ (Endocare. Inc.) is a semirigid penile prosthesis. It is flexible, which makes positioning of the penis quick and easy. The design of the Dura-II™ allows it to bend similar to the flexible metal wire used on a "gooseneck" lamp. The semi-rigid implant is surgically implanted into the corpus cavernosa. During sexual activity the penis can be bent upward into an erect position. As a result, the semi-rigid penile implants will maintain an erection that is well suited for sexual intercourse. During non-sexual activities the penis can be bent down towards the leg eliminating embarrassment from trying to conceal the prosthesis. One drawback of this prosthesis is that the penis remains rigid, meaning that the penis does not return to a fully flaccid state.

In 1973, Dr. F. Brantly Scott developed the inflatable penile prosthesis. The prosthesis consists of three components: a pair of cylinders, a pump, and a reservoir filled with fluid. The entire prosthesis is surgically implanted into the body. The two cylinders are inserted into each of the corpus cavernosa, the pump is placed in the scrotum, and the reservoir is inserted beneath the abdominal muscle. In order to achieve an erection the man squeezes the pump several times, which pushes the fluid out of the reservoir and into the two cylinders resulting in an erection. In order to return the penis to its flaccid state a release valve is pushed causing the fluid to return to the reservoir. There have been reports of men who have experienced an erection and ejaculation using this prosthesis (Auerbash, 1983). There are currently several varieties of inflatable penile prostheses. The two most commonly reported complications of penile implants have been infections and the erosion of the skin of the penis allowing the implant to break through. Both have been reported to occur 8% to 33% of the time (Linsenmeyer, 2000). If you are considering a penile prosthesis consult with your physician as to which one is right for you.

Sildenafil (Viagra™): Sildenafil, better known to many as Viagra™, is an orally prescribed medication. It has become the "wonder drug" for many men who have been suffering from erectile dysfunction. Sildenafil has been very successful in treating erectile dysfunction in non-SCI men. It functions by increasing the amount of cGMP in the corpora cavernosa. The result is a higher concentration of cGMP in the corpora cavernosa causing the smooth muscles to relax allowing blood to flow into the penis resulting in an erection. Recent studies using Sildenafil have begun to focus on treating erectile dysfunction in men with spinal cord injuries. A two-part study was conducted on men with lower level spinal cord injuries (T5 and below) who were able to obtain reflexogenic erections. The study found that those individuals prescribed the Sildenafil had improvement in the rigidity and duration of their erections compared to those in the placebo group. The reported side effects, although mild, were upset stomach and a respiratory disorder (Maytom, Derry, Dinsmore, Glass, Smith, Orr, & Osterloh, 1999). In reviewing the current literature on Sildenafil in treating erectile dysfunction in men with SCI, those individuals who tend to benefit the most are those who have incomplete spinal cord injuries and are able to experience reflexogenic erections. Although Sildenafil has been proven to be successful in the treatment of erectile dysfunction in some men with SCI, it is not a cure, nor does it work for everyone who has tried it. Two reported side effects from using Sildenafil included headaches and flushing. It should be noted that these are all similar side effects of automatic dysreflexia with the exception of severe uncontrolled hypertension. It is very important that you be able to tell the difference because nitrates, often used to treat automatic dysreflexia, if given after taking Sildenafil can cause severe hypotension. Therefore, if you are considering Sildenafil, consult with your physician to determine if this treatment is right for you.

Chapter 5
Male Fertility following an SCI

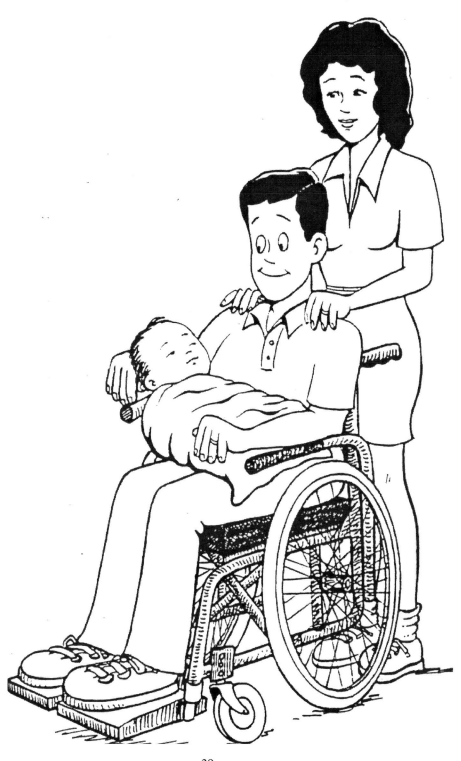

Following a spinal cord injury, one of the major issues regarding sexuality that a man must deal with is whether or not he will be able to father a child. The answer to this question for some men can be rather devastating, resulting in symptoms of depression and a lowered self-esteem. Others may be less affected. How a man with an SCI deals with this issue seems to depend on how old they are when their injury occurs, how important being a father is to them, and whether or not they already have children. If the spinal cord injury occurs while a man is a young child or during his adolescent years, the thought of getting married and having a family is typically far from his mind. However, if the individual is an adult male with a desire to have a child with his female partner or spouse, the answer to this question becomes more important. There comes a point in most serious relationships when a couple has a discussion about having children. Most men with an SCI who have dated or are currently in a relationship will tell you that at some point in their relationship they were asked by their partner about their capability of fathering a child. This is an issue that should be openly discussed and not avoided. Depending on the level of injury and motor neurological functioning, this may not be an easy "yes" or "no" answer. The incidence of male infertility following a spinal cord injury depends on several factors including the level of injury, whether the injury is complete or incomplete, the capability of ejaculation, and sperm quality. Infertility is a common problem in 90% of men with a spinal cord injury. Solving it often requires the use of alternative methods of sperm retrieval. This chapter will concentrate on the causes of male infertility as a result of a spinal cord injury and explore proven sperm retrieval techniques which have successfully resulted in pregnancies.

A word of caution to those of you who are currently sexually active: it is important to keep in mind that despite the decreased risk of impregnating a woman through "typical" vaginal intercourse, you should not see this as an opportunity to have unprotected sexual intercourse. Some men following an SCI develop a sense that they are invincible and therefore protected from catching STDs. Not being able to feel your penis or having the ability to ejaculate during sexual intercourse does not protect you from catching a disease (see Chapter 9). If you and your partner are serious about having a child it is important that both of you be able to openly express your opinions and thoughts about the type of sperm retrieval technique you feel comfortable using. If discussing fertility or sexual issues is difficult for you and your partner, it is recommended that you seek the services of a specialist such as a urologist, a gynocologist, a rehabilitation psychologist, or a counselor who specializes in reproductive and sexual counseling.

Ejaculatory Dysfunction

Two major problems that usually occur in men with an SCI resulting in ejaculatory dysfunction are the loss of the ability to ejaculate and retrograde ejaculations. The inability to ejaculate is the primary cause of infertility in men with spinal cord injuries. Statistically it has been reported that ejaculation occurs 5% of the time in males with complete upper motor neuron injuries, 18% of the time in males with complete lower motor neuron injuries, and 70% of the time in males who have incomplete motor lesions (Scheutzow & Bockenek, 2000).

The exact neurophysiological process for causing an ejaculation is not clearly understood. However, some researchers have proposed that the process of having an ejaculation once sexual stimulation of the penis begins can be divided into three phases. During the first phase prostatic fluid, seminal fluid, and sperm are combined and transferred into the posterior urethra. As the stimulation of the penis continues, the second phase begins when pressure builds within the posterior urethra closing the neck of the bladder. The third stage begins with rhythmic contractions causing the prostate to pump the fluid and sperm through the urethra and expelling it out the tip of the penis.

It has been hypothesized that the reason men with complete SCIs are unable to ejaculate or have decreased ability to ejaculate is that in order for an ejaculation to occur there must be a coordinated neurological impulse from the sympathetic, parasympathetic, and somatic nervous systems. Because neurological impulses cannot be transmitted below the level of injury, this coordinated neurological impulse from the peripheral nervous system is unable to function.

Retrograde Ejaculation

The second major problem which often occurs in men with spinal cord injuries is that they frequently have what is known as retrograde ejaculations. A retrograde ejaculation occurs when the sperm is ejaculated back into the bladder instead of being expelled through the urethra and out the tip of the penis. This occurs because the neurological signals sent to the lower part of the spinal cord at thoracic-12 (T12) and lumbar-1

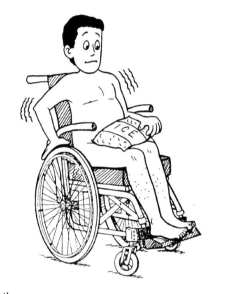

" IMPROVING SPERM QUALITY "

(L1) are unable to tell the muscles of the posterior urethra to close the neck of the bladder (Perkash, 1986). The sperm ejaculated into the bladder is often unable to survive in this environment because of the acidity of the urine. However, with the use of modern day science and technology, physicians are now able to increase sperm survival during a retrograde ejaculation, so that it can be used later for insemination. The individual takes orally prescribed sodium bicarbonate tablets 2 or 3 days prior to removal of the sperm from the bladder. This is done in order to alkalinize his urine. He is then told to induce an ejaculation using the least invasive method. Immediately following ejaculation, the patient empties his bladder either by voiding or catheterization. The sperm collected is medically washed and prepared for insemination. The prepared sperm is then injected using a sterile syringe directly into the area of the cervix (Lizza, 1990).

Figure 5.1 Brrrr!!!

Sperm Quality

In addition to ejaculatory dysfunction, poor sperm quality and sperm motility are other problems faced by men with spinal cord injuries who want to father children. There are many possible causes of poor sperm quality in men with an SCI. These include the stasis (stopping) of prostatic fluid, drug or alcohol abuse, cigarette smoking, testicular hyperthermia, urinary tract infections, sperm that comes in contact with urine, long term use of medications, and the type of bladder management. The exact impact or importance of any single factor on sperm quality is not known. It is more likely that a combination of these factors causes poor sperm quality (Perkash, 1986, Linsenmeyer & Perkash, 1991).

A special note of interest to those individuals who use a strap to keep their legs together or who prefer to sit in their wheelchair

Figure 5.2 The Future Fertility Seat Cushion

with their legs close together: using a leg strap or sitting with your legs close together can adversely affect sperm quality and motility. The leg strap prevents the scrotum from being able to control the temperature within the testes. As a result, the temperature within the testes may become elevated to limits which decrease sperm production. One researcher reported that one of his male subjects improved his sperm count by applying ice packs on his scrotum several times a day to lower his scrotal temperature (see Figure 5.1). Unfortunately many of us with SCIs do not have the luxury of sitting around with an ice pack on our scrotum because we and our significant other want to have a child. However, in the near future someone may invent a fertility seat cushion for wheelchairs with a built in refrigeration unit (see Figure 5.2). Until such a seat cushion is created, reducing scrotal temperature may be possible by propping your legs apart and wearing loose clothing. But men with SCIs can take other steps to improve the quality and motility of their sperm. The first and most important factor is to try to prevent or at least minimize urinary tract infections. In other words, drink lots of water and develop good hygiene habits. Second, if you contract a urinary tract infection, ask your treating physician to prescribe an antibiotic that is non-toxic to sperm. In fact, if you are taking any medications, you may want to ask your physician if they are harmful to sperm. Third, it is important to avoid sperm stagnation, especially in the lower storage sites in the testes. This can be accomplished through regular sexual activity resulting in an ejaculation. Weekly sexual activity can significantly improve sperm quality, motility, and increase the sperm count.

Bladder Management

Research has found that the method of bladder management can affect sperm count and motility. Men with spinal cord injuries who perform low pressure methods such as intermittent catheterization (ISC) to empty their bladder, had an overall higher total sperm count and a higher number of motile sperm than those men using other forms of bladder management such as reflex voiding. When men with an SCI using ISC bladder management were compared to men with an SCI using reflex voiding as bladder management (the most common alternative to ISC), it was found that ISC users had a significantly higher percentage of motile sperm and a higher sperm count (Ohl, Menge, & Sonksen). Intermittent catheterization is definitely better.

As stated above, urinary tract infections (UTI) can have adverse effects on fertility and sperm motility. However, researchers have not been able to fully understand how a UTI affects sperm quality (Linsenmeyer & Perkash, 1991). Unfortunately, every man with an SCI will at some point in his life experience a UTI. Good bladder management, drinking plenty of water, and good hygiene habits can help to reduce your risks of developing a UTI. Check with your rehabilitation nurse or treating physician for advise as to what is the best way for you to prevent a UTI.

Fertility Techniques

Most men with spinal cord injuries will require the use of assisted ejaculation techniques if they desire to father children. The purpose of using these techniques is so that semen can be obtained and used to impregnate their female partner either naturally or artificially. Currently there are five types of sperm retrieval techniques:

- Electroejaculation.
- Penile vibratory stimulation.
- Intrathecal neostigmine-induced ejaculations.

42

- Intravaginal voiding.
- Frenulum trigger.

Electroejaculation: The most common and most successful treatment for infertility in men with spinal cord injuries is electroejaculation. Research has found that the success rate of electroejaculation causing an ejaculation in men with spinal cord injuries is 85% to 100% (Brackett, Pardron, & Lynne, 1997). During the procedure the individual is placed on his back, and a rectal probe (electrode) is inserted into the rectum (see Figure 5.3). (Most physicians will request that a bowel program be performed the evening prior to or the morning of the procedure to insure the rectum is empty before the procedure begins.) The probe is placed near the seminal vesicles, prostate, and vas deferens. A rectal thermometer is inserted next to the probe in order to measure the rectal temperature during the procedure. Rectal tissue is very sensitive and can easily be damaged

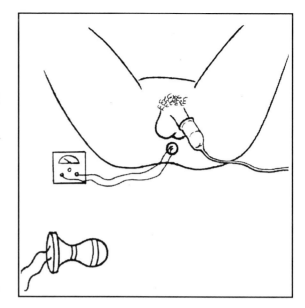

Figure 5.3 Electroejaculation

or burned therefore, the temperature of the rectum is monitored and prevented from rising above 99° F. In addition to rectal temperature, the medical staff monitors the patient's heart rate and blood pressure before, during, and after the procedure. Once the probe has been properly positioned, electrostimulation is applied for 2 seconds at a time. The procedure is continued until ejaculation occurs or until a maximum of 5 trial stimulations have been administered. If the individual does not have an ejaculation following 5 trials, it is recommended the individual undergo a complete urological exam to rule out any possible congenital or obstructive pathology (Lizza, 1990, Leyson, 1990).

It should be pointed out that there have been several reported complications as a result of using electroejaculation. The most common side effects include severe headaches, sweating of the face and neck, flushing of the skin, and autonomic dysreflexia, which is a rapid increase in blood pressure. If the individual is prone to autonomic dysreflexia, the condition can be prevented in most cases by a physician administering 10 to 20 mg of nifedipine (a calcium channel blocker) prior to the stimulation. There have also been a number of reported cases of hypertension occurring in men with cervical spinal cord injuries (C7 and above). This can be controlled with prostaglandin E_2. Another drawback of using electroejaculation is the low volume of sperm recovered following the procedure. There was one reported case in-which a 23-year-old, C-6 quadriplegic male developed autonomic dysreflexia which developed into atrial fibrillation following the use of electroejaculation. The individual was transferred to the emergency department where the medical staff was able to return the patient to a normal sinus rhythm using medications (Scheutzow & Bockeneck, 2000).

Penile Vibratory Stimulation: This technique involves the use a vibrator to stimulate the glans and frenulum of the penis until a reflex ejaculation occurs. Research indicates that penile vibratory stimulation has been successful in 75% to 80% of men with an SCI using this technique. The greatest success occurs in those men with an injury above T10 who use a high amplitude vibrator (Brackett, Pardron, & Lynne, 1997). Some men with SCIs have found that vibrators sold in adult stores or purchased through mail order are sufficient in aiding them to have an ejaculation (see Chapter 8). A study found that the use of store or mail ordered vibrators resulted in a 30% success rate for causing ejaculations (Lensenmeyer, 2000). However, most men with SCIs will need to use a specialty vibrator, such as the FERT CARE personal, (see Photo 5.1) which has been specifically developed to help men with ejaculation dysfunction to have a reflex ejaculation. These vibrators can be purchased with a prescription from a physician.

The procedure for using penile vibratory stimulation begins by placing the individual in a reclined position or seated in his wheelchair. The vibrator is placed on the frenulum or shaft of the penis for a maximum of 3 minutes. This is followed by a pause of 1 to 2 minutes. The procedure is repeated for a total of 4 to 6 cycles or until an ejaculation occurs. The semen obtained from using this procedure can then be injected into the vagina using a syringe or injected directly into the cervix using a cannula. Some couples, in the privacy of their own home, have even used a "turkey" baster, which can be purchased in any local store that sells kitchen utensils, to inject the semen into the women's vagina. Penile stimulation should be discontinued if the individual begins to experience autonomic dysreflexia or the skin around the area of stimulation becomes irritated. If a reflex ejaculation does not occur, it is possible that a retrograde ejaculation has.

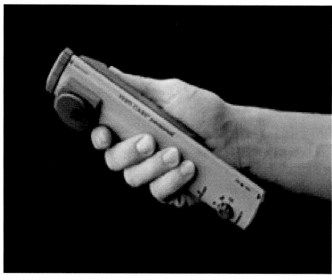

Photo 5.1 Ferti Care Personal Vibrator

Common side effects reported using this technique are similar to those experienced with electroejaculation, including headaches, sweating, flushing of the skin, and autonomic dysreflexia. As stated above, if you are prone to autonomic dysreflexia taking nifedipine prior to vibratory stimulation can help to prevent this condition. Men with an SCI above T5 should try to be aware of their blood pressure during the procedure. In addition to these side effects, some men have reported swelling of the shaft of their penis around the area of stimulation directly following the use of this technique. The swelling will usually subside within a few hours. However, if the swelling continues, medical attention should be sought.

One advantage of using penile vibratory stimulation is that semen quality is better when compared to semen quality from using electroejaculation. Another advantage is that, this technique results in the semen being expelled from the body in a somewhat "normal" fashion, and therefore it is free from contamination of urine.

A special note of interest for those men with spinal cord injuries who have or are considering a penile prosthesis and are currently using penile vibratory stimulation. A study was conducted on 26 men with spinal cord injuries whose lesions were above T10 and who were undergoing fertility treatment using penile vibratory stimulation. Five of the men who participated in the study had a penile prosthesis. The result showed that only 2 of the 5 men (40%) with a prosthesis experienced an antegrade ejaculation using this procedure, whereas 19 of 21 men (90%) without the prosthesis experienced an antegrade ejaculation. The researchers hypothesized that the implantation of the prosthesis may have resulted in diminished sensory input into the reflex arc. This was likely caused by subtle damage to the dorsal nerves of the penis. Since an antegrade ejaculation requires an intact reflex arc and functioning dorsal nerves of the penis, such an injury to the dorsal nerves could reduce the effectiveness of penile vibratory stimulation (Ohl, Menge, and

Sonksen).

Intrathecal Neostigmine-induced Ejaculations: A number of pharmacologic agents such as intrathecal neostigmine have been successful in causing men with SCIs to have erections and ejaculations. However, the exact nature of how neostigmine causes these erections and ejaculations to occur is not known. A study was conducted on 5 men with spinal cord lesions ranging from C4 to T12 using intrathecal neostigmine. Following the injection of neostigmine, erections occurred in 60% of the men, and four of the five men (80%) experienced an ejaculation. The sperm recovered was then used to inseminate their spouses. In a larger study using 70 men with SCIs and intrathecal neostigmine there was a 59.7% success rate of ejaculations occurring. However, because of the severity of the side effects this procedure was often performed in the intensive care unit. Reported side effects included nausea, vomiting, headaches, drowsiness, retention of urine, and a high incidence of autonomic dysreflexia, that could result in death due to cerebral hemorrhage. In fact, researchers recommended that men with SCIs who have a severe cardiovascular disease or a history of strokes avoid this fertility technique. Although the success rates for using intrathecal neostigmine have been rather high, the severity of the side effects have caused the discontinuation of use of this technique in the United States. (Lizza, 1990, Linsenmeyer, 2000).

Intravaginal Voiding: Some couples may want to try a non-medical intervention for vaginal insemination. One option is a technique known as postejaculatory intravaginal voiding. This technique is especially useful for those individuals who experience retrograde ejaculations. The technique involves the man voiding or emptying his bladder into his partner's vagina following sexual stimulation. Although this method may seem somewhat unorthodox, it has been proven to be a rather successful technique resulting in pregnancies. A study was conducted using this technique with eight males with SCIs and their female partners. The men with SCIs who participated in the study included three paraplegics, two quadriplegics with complete spinal cord injuries, and three quadriplegics with incomplete spinal cord injuries. When the study was concluded, two paraplegics and one quadriplegic with an incomplete injury were successful in impregnating their wives (Leyson, 1990).

The best time to use this technique is when the woman is ovulating, which is the most fertile period of her menstrual cycle. The technique begins with alkalinization of the male's urine 2 to 3 days prior to using this technique by orally taking prescription sodium bicarbonate. The next step involves the man emptying his bladder either by voiding or catheterization, two or three hours prior to sexual activity. Before engaging in sexual activity, the man drinks 750 to 800 mL of water to fill his bladder to prevoiding volume. During this same time period it is highly recommended that the woman uses an alkaline vaginal douche, which helps to increase the survival rate of the sperm. The couple then engages in sexual activity. After the man experiences postejaculatory or orgasmic sensations, he empties the contents of his bladder by voiding into his partner's vagina. The woman lies on her back with her pelvis elevated for 60 to 90 minutes. This assists the sperm in moving towards and into her cervix. Afterwards, the woman allows the urine to drain from her vagina.

It is important to understand that this method is not "dirty" or physically harmful to either partner, assuming that neither has poor hygiene habits or an STD. Although this technique sounds messy, with some preplanning the mess and cleanup can be kept to a minimum. If you are interested in trying this technique, for starters use a plastic fitted sheet on your bed to protect the mattress. If you do not have a plastic fitted sheet, try using a disposable underpad, towels, or several layered sheets of newspaper placed on top of the bed and under your partner's pelvic region prior to voiding into her vagina. It would also be a good idea to keep several bath towels next to the bed just in case you need them.

I would just like to give a few words of comfort to your female partner. Remember, the reason you and your partner are trying this technique is that you want to have a baby. You should not feel ashamed or humiliated because you are using this method to achieve pregnancy.

Frenulum Trigger: Some men with upper level SCIs have reported having the ability to have an antegrade ejaculation by masterbating even though they retain the ability to have only reflexagenic erections. This technique tends to work best if you understand what causes your body to achieve a reflexagenic erection. For instance, some individuals can cause reflexogenic erections by bending their knees outward so that their feet come together while lying comfortably on their back stretching their groin muscles. Other individuals have noted that their leg muscles spasm more during a certain time of the day making it easier to obtain and maintain a reflexagenic erection (see Chapter 4 for information on methods of obtaining an erection).

This technique works best if you are in a comfortable position, usually lying on your back or stretched out in your wheelchair. Begin by stroking the shaft of your penis. If because of the level of your injury you have limited hand grip or no hand grip at all, ask your partner to stroke the shaft of the penis for you (see Figure 5.4).

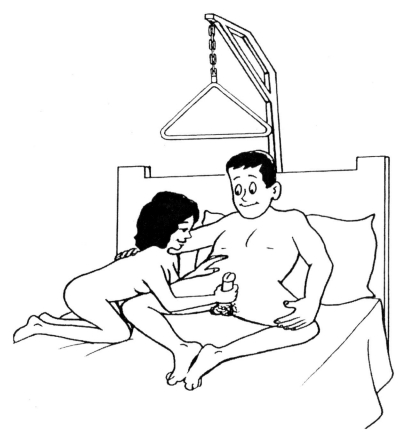

Figure 5.4 "Pulling the Trigger" - The Frenulum Trigger Technique

During this stage of the technique, concentrate only on stroking the shaft of the penis. What you are trying to accomplish during this phase is increasing the vascongestive pressure, which naturally causes the tissues in the penis to engorge with blood resulting in an erection, enlargement of the testes, and an increase in pressure. At some point the built up pressure will reach a threshold causing rhythmic contractions usually felt within the stomach, legs and groin regions. When you begin to experience this pressure and contractions, have your partner begin stroking the area where the glans and shaft come together and where the frenulum is located (See Chapter 2). The strokes should be firm, short, and quick back and forth with emphasis on the forward stroke. This has been called "pulling the trigger" by some. If your body is prepared to have an orgasm, you should experience an ejaculation. If an ejaculation does not occur, return to stroking the shaft of the penis and begin the process again (Ellis, 1980). Individuals who are able to use this technique have noted that the time period from start to ejaculation varies. Everyone's body is different, and the only way to determine if this technique will work for you is to give it a try either alone or with your partner.

It should be noted that this technique seems to be rather body sensitive, which can easily be hampered by factors such as emotions, level of stress, alcohol, drugs, and prescribed medications. When using this technique, one should consider using a water-soluble lubricant (see Chapter 8) which will help to prevent any minor skin abrasions or swelling. Some men have reported short term swelling of the shaft of their penis directly following the use of this technique, but the swelling usually subsides within a few hours. If the swelling continues, medical attention should be sought.

In summary, the two most commonly used fertility techniques are electroejaculation and penile vibratory stimulation. Electroejaculation requires the presence of medical staff to perform the procedure and to monitor the male's vital signs, whereas penile vibratory stimulation is less invasive and can be performed either in a hospital or clinic by the medical staff or in the privacy of one's home. If the man with the SCI has an intact sacral cord, (upper level SCI lesions) many physicians will recommend that the couple begin by trying penile vibratory stimulation. If this method fails to cause an ejaculation, then they will recommend the use of electroejaculation. On the other hand, if the male is unable to obtain a reflex erection or does not have an intact sacral cord, (lower level SCI lesions) the physician may recommend electroejaculation first. Research has discovered that generally semen obtained using penile vibratory stimulation is of better quality than sperm obtained using electroejaculation. To be more specific, they found that sperm motility was significantly greater when using penile vibratory stimulation. However, sperm count, regardless of which technique was used, remained about the same (Lizza, 1990). If neither technique is successful, the physician may attempt to aspirate sperm from the vas deferens, epididymis, or do a biopsy of the testicle. If the physician is still unable to obtain sperm another option is a sperm donor insemination

Insemination Techniques

It would be inappropriate to end this chapter without briefly mentioning the commonly used insemination techniques which have helped men with spinal cord injuries to become fathers. As stated above, 90% of men with spinal cord injuries will require the use of assisted ejaculation techniques to obtain sperm to be used to inseminate their spouses. Approximately 40% of those men with SCIs who have attempted to father children using fertilization techniques have been successful. The most commonly used methods of artificial insemination include:

- Self-Insemination.
- Natural Cycle/Intrauterine Insemination.
- Clomiphene/Intrauterine Insemination.
- Human Menopausal Gonadotropine/Intrauterine Insemination.
- Gamete Intrafallopian Transfer.
- In Vitro Fertilization

The simplest method of assisted fertilization is intrauterine insemination (IUI). Intrauterine insemination involves inserting the sperm into the woman's uterus. The success rate of IUI has been between 10% and 14% in achieving pregnancies. In vitro fertilization (IVF) involves the joining of the male's sperm and woman's egg outside the woman's body. Once the sperm fertilizes the egg, the embryo is placed into the woman's uterus. The success rate of using IVF has been reported at 30% to 40%. However, if the man has sperm with poor motility as a result of their injury then IVF is not an option. Instead a new technique called intracytoplasmic sperm injection (ICSI) is used. In this technique a single sperm is injected directly into the ovum. The advantage of this technique is that it can be use when the individual produces only a few sperm even if motility is poor. It is important to note that there is the possibility of having multiple births when using assisted fertility techniques because usually more than one fertilized ovum is placed in the uterus in the hope that at least one of them will develop into a fetus (Nehra, Werner, Bastuba, Title, & Oats, 1996).

It is important that you and your partner discuss how long each of you are committed to trying to become pregnant. The process can be an emotional roller coaster that requires you to invest time, patience, and money as you attempt to obtain your goal of having a child. If you and your partner are unsure about which method is right for you meet with a specialist and discuss which methods they feel will give you the maximum opportunity to become pregnant. Most specialists require a physical exam for you and your partner in order to determine which method(s) will be right for you. As researchers continue to improve and develop new fertility techniques the number of successful pregnancies and childbirths to men with SCIs will continue to increase.

Adoption

If attempts to become pregnant fail another option for a couple desiring a child is adoption. The issue of adopting a child should be discussed with your partner when the two of you first begin discussing wanting to have children. The process of adopting a child takes time, patience, and money. It may require a lot of paperwork and having to be placed on a waiting list. If you and your partner are seriously considering adopting a child start the process early. Couples wanting to be considered by an agency to adopt a child should have the following: a sincere desire to adopt a child, financial stability, a safe and stable physical environment, and an outside support system. For information and assistance regarding adopting a child contact: The North American Council on Adoptable Children (NACAC). The address to the National office of NACAC is located at 1346 Connecticut Avenue, NW, Suite 229, Washington, DC 20036. In addition you can contact the local offices of Lutheran Social Services and Catholic Charities to inquire about children for adoption.

Parenting Issues for Men with Spinal Cord Injuries

The ability to become a parent is often an important issue for men with SCIs who want to have children and a family. A study was conducted comparing adult children raised from the age of two and younger by fathers with spinal cord injuries to adult children raised by fathers without SCIs. The result of the study showed that adult children of fathers with SCIs were as psychologically well-adjusted as those adult children of fathers without SCIs. This study found no evidence that children with fathers with SCIs suffered any adverse affects from peers or others as a result of their father's disability. What was interesting was that the study found that children raised by fathers with SCIs had a significantly more positive attitude toward their father and they responded more quickly and positively to their parents than did those children raised by fathers without SCIs (Linsenmeyer, 2000).

Chapter 6
What is Oral Sex?

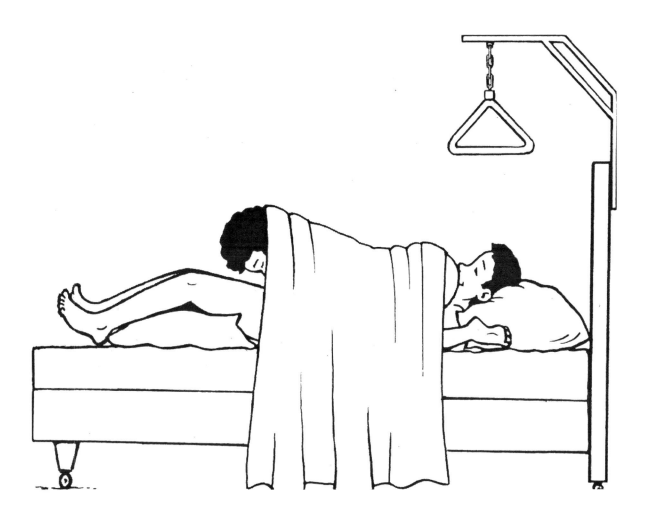

For much of the past, the subject of oral sex has been taboo in our society. We have been told that people who engage in oral sex are sick, perverted, or sex addicts. In some states, oral sex is actually considered a criminal offense. These laws stem from the days of the Puritans, and lawmakers have not gotten around to rescinding them. Our parents told us as children that our genitals are dirty, yucky, and full of germs. In reality, our mouths have more germs and bacteria than our genitals if we keep our genitals clean on a daily basis. As a result, oral sex, like drinking during prohibition, has not been discussed openly and something most people would not admit to trying or practicing.

At the same time individuals with spinal cord injuries are often told that oral sex can greatly enhance their sexual pleasure. In the rehabilitation center you might hear the nurses or therapists mentioning oral sex as an option. However, they don't tell you anything about oral sex. Where do you go to learn about oral sex? What are your options? You could rent the movie "Coming Home" starring Jane Fonda and Jon Voight and watch a steamy five minute love scene of a man with an SCI performing oral sex on an able-bodied woman. Another option is that you could go to the local adult video store and rent a couple of X-rated videos. However, there is always a certain stigma associated with visiting such places. Besides, many of them are not wheelchair accessible. Imagine, getting your wheelchair stuck in the door of your local adult video store and having a little old lady, who reminds you of your grandmother, trying to help you through the door (see Figure 6.1). Consequently, I will save you the embarrassment by writing this chapter on oral sex, which you may read in the privacy of your own home.

Figure 6.1 Not again!!!

The purpose of this chapter is to introduce you to the techniques of oral sex, reduce your concerns or fears, and answer questions you may have. Oral sex is a wonderful experience to share with your partner. It is a technique that takes time and patience to learn. The ability to be able to perform oral sex well on your partner is not something that you learn to do overnight. You must be able to openly communicate with your partner. You must also listen to your partner. You need to be aware of how her body responds as she becomes aroused and arrives at the point of orgasm. It is a beautiful experience and well worth the time and effort put into learning how to achieve it. We will begin by exploring how your partner can perform oral sex on you. We will address the concerns you may have such as what to do if you wear an external catheter, a leg bag, or a night drainage bag; how to prevent bladder accidents; and what to do if one occurs. Then we will explore ways for you to perform oral sex on your partner. But before we begin, it is important to discuss some simple ground rules with your partner. Once again the issue of open communication is very important.

Ground Rules & Helpful Hints

- Do not bite your partner's genitals with your teeth. The genitals are a very sensitive part of the body. The genitals will bleed profusely if the skin is broken. So **no biting**.
- Keep you fingernails trimmed. A sharp nail can cut your partner causing them to bleed.
- **Never** blow air into your partner's genitals. This can be very dangerous, especially if the air gets into the bloodstream. This does not mean that you can't breathe while performing oral sex on your partner but it does mean that she cannot be blowing air into your penis and you cannot be blowing air up into her vagina during oral sex.
- Trim or shave your pubic hair. There is nothing worse than coughing up a hairball or stopping as she is about to orgasm to remove a hair from your mouth. It can kill the mood. Trimming or shaving your partner in itself can be an erotic experience.
- Keep your genitals clean. The body naturally sweats throughout the day and has its own odors, some of which are not at all pleasant. No one wants to perform oral sex on someone who smells. Wash your genitals daily with mild soap and water. Try to avoid soaps with perfumes since they may irritate the genitals. Women do not need to wash the inside of their vaginas.
- If you wear an external catheter, be sure to have your partner wash the extra tape and skin prep off the genitals before they perform oral sex on you. I have been told that skin prep, alcohol prep, and the powder from the externals are not very appetizing. Nor is it a pleasant experience for your partner to try to perform oral sex on a penis that has been in an external all day long. The best time for having oral sex is after a shower and before the external is put on when your whole body is clean. Be considerate of your partner.
- Always keep a urinal beside the bed just in case of an emergency. There is the possibility that your bladder might be triggered, and you want to be prepared.
- If there is any chance that you or your partner has any sexually transmitted disease, take precautions (see Chapter 9).

The Male Receiving Oral Sex

The technical term for oral stimulation of the penis is *fellatio*. However, it is also commonly called a "blow job", "giving head", or "going down on him". Before I say any more you may be asking yourself, "If I can't feel my penis, maintain an erection, or have an orgasm because of my spinal cord injury, why do I need to consider oral sex for myself?" It is true that many males with a spinal cord injury, regardless of their level of injury, will not be able to feel their partner performing fellatio. It is also true, that because of the level of your injury, you may not be able to have an orgasm. However, it may be possible to obtain an erection through oral stimulation which could be hard enough to use for masturbation or vaginal penetration.

Even though you may not be able to feel your partner performing fellatio, it is highly erotic watching them. You may also discover that you do have some feeling and that receiving oral sex is relaxing, stimulating, and may even reduce spasms. Think of it as watching an X-rated video live. Never discourage your partner from wanting to perform oral sex because of your lack of feeling and sensitivity in the penis. Just try it; you may like it a lot.

Before having oral sex remove or have your partner remove your external if you wear one. If you empty your bladder using a catheter, it is better to empty your bladder before engaging in sexual activity. You don't want to accidentally urinate in your partner's mouth. Again, one of the best times to have oral sex is following a shower when the genitals are the cleanest (see Bowel and Bladder Issues in Chapter 3). The best position for oral sex is for the male to lie on his back (see Figure 6.2). This allows the woman to find a position that is the most comfortable for her. Pillows can be placed under the male's back to enable him to watch. The important thing is to be sure that both of you are comfortable.

How to Perform Oral Sex: From Her to Him: For many men having their penis sucked by their partner is the ultimate sexual fantasy come true. This is also the ultimate sexual fantasy for many males with SCIs. It is very erotic for a male to watch his partner suck his penis. If this is your first time performing oral sex on a man, begin by kissing his penis. Kiss around the head (glans) and the shaft of the penis. It is all right to hold the penis while you're kissing it; however, be aware of your grip because your partner with the SCI may not be able to tell how hard you are squeezing. A rule of thumb, if the head starts turning red or blue, it is strongly recommended that you loosen your grip. Also, as your partner's penis becomes erect, be careful not to bend it. The penis will naturally bend upwards towards his chest, but bending the penis downward can bring discomfort and pain to your partner.

Begin by using your tongue to lick up and down the shaft of the penis. Lick the head of the penis and allow your tongue to flicker across the opening of the urethra. Swirl and flicker your tongue over the frenulum, which is located on the underside of the head of the penis where the shaft meets the glans. This area is very sensitive and, for some men with an SCI constant stimulation may result in an orgasm (see Chapter 2). Experiment with various strokes. Allow your lips to take his penis into your mouth and begin a gentle, rhythmic sucking of the penis. Use your lips and tongue to suck on the glans and shaft of the penis while pushing his penis in and out of your mouth. Try to simulate the motion of having intercourse. If your partner's penis is too large try holding the shaft of the penis while sucking it. You can also use your hands to masturbate your partner or lightly massage his testicles, his chest, or other areas of his body. You can also insert a finger into his anus. However be sure your nails are not sharp or that you don't stimulate his bowels. You can also suck or lick his testicles by taking them into your mouth. Take your time and listen to your partner's responses to your actions. Experiment with different combinations to discover what feels best to him. Watch his body and listen to what he says.

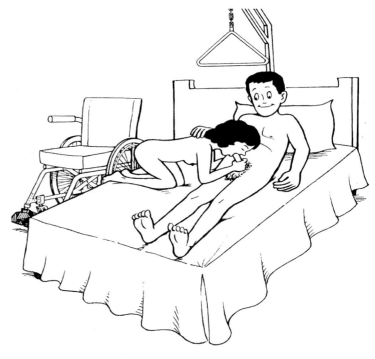

Figure 6.2 'From Her to Him'

If your partner with an SCI does not have an orgasm, don't become discouraged and don't feel that you're unable to sexually please him. Many males with SCIs cannot experience an orgasm as a result of their injury. If you become discouraged talk to your partner. Let them know your concerns. However, you may find that your partner will experience great pleasure and satisfaction by watching and experiencing your orgasm.

The Female Receiving Oral Sex

The technical term for oral stimulation of the clitoris is *cunnilingus*. It has also been termed "eating her out" or "muff diving." Basically, cunnilingus is making love to your partner's genitals by using your lips and tongue. Many women have had their best orgasms through oral sex. Learning to perform oral sex on your partner takes time, patience, and prac-

Figure 6.3 'From Him to Her' while laying on her back.

Figure 6.4 'From Him to Her' while sitting over her partner's face this position allows the woman to control and direct her partner's tongue right where she wants it.

tice. The rewards for learning the techniques of oral sex will be well worth the effort. A woman likes to know that her sexual needs are as important to you as they are to her. Wanting to please them orally is seen by many women as the ultimate expression of love. In a way oral sex can equalize the playing field between a man with an SCI and a man without a spinal cord injury. Many women tend to prefer a man who can perform oral sex well over a man with a large penis. In a recent study conducted by Anne Guldin, a male subject with a spinal cord injury, when questioned about his beliefs on oral sex, commented that he felt his disability gave him an advantage over non-disabled men. In his opinion, non-disabled men were less likely to perform and enjoy oral sex on a woman. And if the non-disabled individual does perform oral sex on his female partner, it is so the act will be reciprocated. It is his belief and experience that the tongue can bring about greater pleasure for a woman than can a penis. In addition, this individual stated he likes to take his time performing oral sex on his partners, which makes the experience more rewarding for both of them. In summary, a man, regardless if he has a disability or a large penis, who is willing to be patient, sensitive, move slowly, and focus more on giving pleasure to the woman's entire body will be the more desirable sexual partner (Guldin, 2000).

How to Perform Oral Sex: From Him to Her: Before we begin, it is important to mention some simple rules. First, don't go straight for the genitals. Second, don't rush. Take your time and enjoy yourself. Third, it is helpful to have knowledge of the female sexual anatomy. If you skipped through the female anatomy section in Chapter 2, **shame on you!!!** Go back and review this section. It helps a lot if you know what you're looking at and what you're looking for. Fourth, if your partner has an unpleasant odor, before having oral sex with her, ask her to wash her genitals or wait until after she showers. You both want this to be a pleasant experience. Finally, some women may have a lot of pubic hair which can be stiff and create an unpleasant experience in which you may have to stop to remove a hair from your mouth or you may gag on a hair that you have swallowed. Talk to your partner about the possibility of trimming or shaving her pubic hair. Shaving her pubic hair together can be a highly erotic experience for both of you.

I recommend that the room be somewhat lit, even if it is just a dim light. It is better to be able to see what you are doing. A lit room helps you to see which area of her genitals you are stimulating. Moreover, I highly recommend that you be aware of where your leg bag, night bag, and/or urinal are located. You don't want to pinch a tube and cause a leak or blockage. If you are naked and in bed, it is a good idea to have your urinal close at hand. It is possible that while performing oral sex on your partner, your bladder may trigger and need to be emptied. Always be prepared for what might happen. It is also good to know where your wheelchair, trapeze, and other assisted devices are located within the room if you need to move around, especially after you have transferred to the bed. If your partner is lying on her back, place a pillow under her hips. This will raise her body and give you better access to her genitals. The pillow will also help you to avoid straining your neck muscles.

Speaking of strain, it is important that you be in a comfortable position when performing on your partner. It can be done from the wheelchair while she lies on the bed or on a table. If you transfer to a bed, there are various positions you can use (see Figure 6.3). It is important that both you and your partner are comfortable. If you have limited use of your arms, position your body so that your arms don't become tired or numb from leaning on them for a long period of time. You and your partner will have to experiment with different positions. It is always a good idea to use various positions so that your body does not tire. If you are a quadriplegic, a good position for you is to lie on your back with a pillow under your head and have your partner kneel over your face (see Figure 6.4). Your partner can either face towards you or away from you, giving you different angles for stimulating her genitals. These positions will also enable your partner to position her genitals where she wants you to stimulate them and allow her to control the amount of pressure she wants applied.

As stated above in the simple rules don't go straight for her genitals. It is best to build up the excitement. Start by kissing around her head. Women tend to be sensitive around the ears, the mouth, the cheeks, and the sides of the neck. Some women enjoy having their ear lobes and neck nibbled.

Note: Nibbling involves the use of your lips as you lightly nip at your partner's skin. Nibbling does not involve using your teeth. The idea is not to bite her; the idea is to excite her. Another word of advice, don't try to give her a "hickie" or "sucker bite" on the neck. The idea is to demonstrate affection and arouse her, not brand her. Marking your partner is for kids, not adults.

Slowly work your way down to her breasts. Kiss her breasts and use your tongue to tease her nipples. Flicker your tongue over her nipple and be aware of it becoming erect. Allow her nipple to enter your mouth and gently suck it. While you are stimulating one breast with your mouth you can use your hand to stimulate the other breast. You might also try going back and forth kissing each breast. Next, slowly begin to descend toward her belly button. Kiss and stroke her tummy. Now kiss the insides of her thighs, the back of her knees, or her ankles. Allow your lips to brush over her pubic mound (mons pubis). Your warm breath will help to increase her anticipation. Run your lips or tongue across her outer lips. Suck on her outer lips by taking one or the other into your mouth. Part her outer lips with your tongue to allow yourself to lick her inner lips. Use your tongue to lick around the opening of the vagina and flick your tongue in and out of the vagina. Use your tongue to make long flat strokes or short fast strokes. Repeat what you have been doing if you like. But remember to listen to what you partner tells you and watch for nonverbal cues such as moaning or grinding of the hips.

The most sensitive area of a woman's genitals is her clitoris (see Chapter 2). Direct stimulation of the clitoris if done too quickly or too soon, or with too much pressure can be very uncomfortable and even painful for a woman. Because of this don't go straight for the clitoris. In the beginning, lightly lick and tease the clitoris. As your partner becomes aroused, she will be able to tolerate more direct stimulation of the clitoris. Some women like to have their clitoris sucked and licked. Using your tongue to provide direct rhythmic pressure to the clitoris could cause your partner to have an orgasm.

While you are orally stimulating your partner's genitals, use your free hand to caress her breasts, tummy, the inside of her legs, or other body parts. Try holding her vaginal lips apart with one of your hands while orally stimulating her. If you have difficulty doing this, ask your partner to help. Another option would be to insert a finger or two into her vagina while orally stimulating her. If you are a quadriplegic and unable to move your fingers, once again ask your partner to help you. There is no harm or shame in asking for help. After all, you are doing this to please her. You can also insert a finger into her anus, especially as she nears orgasm. Just be sure your fingernails are not sharp and be sure to use lubrication on your finger.

Warning: Do not put anything that has been in the anus into the vagina. This increases the possibility of your partner getting an infection.

There are also various sexual aids (see chapter 8) that can be used while performing oral sex to enhance the sexual experience. The important thing to keep in mind is that there are many ways to please your partner. Take your time and explore what she likes. Listen to what she says. If she tells you that what you are doing feels really good or that she likes what you're doing, make a mental note of it for future reference. As the woman nears her orgasm and she says, "Don't stop," be a good sport and don't stop!

As your partner becomes excited, you will notice that her vagina becomes wet. This is known as vaginal fluids and is a natural form of lubrication. It is safe to lick and swallow these fluids. Many men enjoy the taste of their partner's vaginal fluids. Some men have noted that these fluids tend to change in taste, depending upon their partner's menstrual cycle. Let your partner know that you like how she tastes. Make sounds like "Mmm...," letting her know that you like what you're doing. Some women like to hear a man talk "dirty" to them. If this is the case, it is recommended that the two of you have a discussion at some point as to what words are acceptable vs. those that are not.

What should you do once your partner has had her orgasm? Once you have stopped stimulating her genitals some suggested options would include the following. Lay your head on her thigh while her body recovers. Move up along side of her and cuddle with her by holding her in your arms. Have a light conversation about how good it felt. Some women are able to have multiple orgasms and after a few minutes are quite able to have oral sex again and have another orgasm. Listen to your partner and if she is willing and you have the strength by all means continue on. The important thing is to enjoy each other's company and have a good time together.

Performing Oral Sex on Her During Her Menstrual Period: Many men when it comes to oral sex and his partner's menstrual period will ask the question: **Is it possible to perform oral sex on my partner when she is having her menstrual period?** The answer to this question is **Yes.** It is not harmful for you to perform oral sex on your partner during her menstrual period. The blood from her menstrual period is not harmful to your health unless she has an STD, is HIV positive, or has AIDS. The fact of the matter is that oral sex during her period can actually reduce her menstrual cramps. The orgasm caused by oral sex allows her muscles to relax, thus reducing her cramps. If your partner or you are not comfortable with oral sex during her menstrual period, don't try to force the issue. Respect each other's decision.

The "69" Position

The "69" position involves both partners performing oral sex on each other at the same time (see Figure 6.5). This position tends to work best if you lie on your back and allow your partner to be on top. It is a good idea to place a pillow under your head and knees for support and comfort. With your partner on top, there are two ways of gaining access to her genitals. In the first position her knees are behind your shoulders (Figure 6.6). This position requires that you spread her lips with your hands to be able to stimulate her clitoris. You can also expose her anus, which may increase her pleasure. The second position involves placing your arms around the outside of her legs (see Figure 6.7). This position tends to give you more control, and it naturally exposes her genitals allowing easy access to her inner lips, her vagina, and her clitoris. This position also helps you to control the amount of weight your

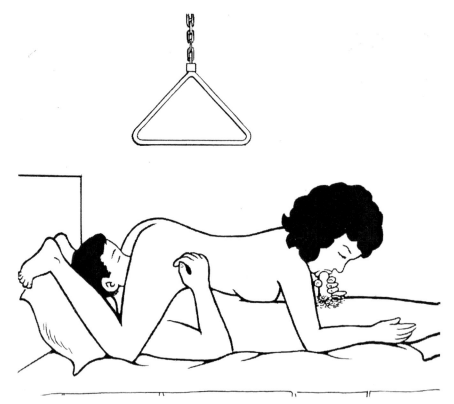

Figure 6.5 The '69' Position where both partners give and receive simultaneously.

56

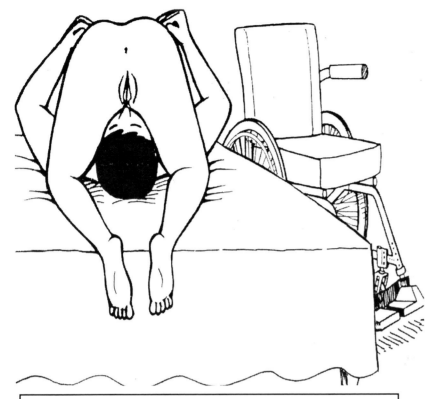

partner is placing on your chest. In the "69" position your partner can orally stimulate your penis while you orally stimulate her. While in this position you can use your free hands to rub her back, her buttocks, or her thighs. It is also possible in this position to insert a finger or some type of sexual aide into her anus or her vagina while you're performing oral sex. If your partner's weight or your pressure sores are a concern, try doing the "69" position while lying on your side. If you have difficulty staying on your side, try using various sized pillows to prop yourself. Experiment a little and find what positions are the most comfortable for both of you.

Now that we have explored ways

Figure 6.6 'Her Knees Behind Your Shoulders Position'. This position gives the woman more control.

of pleasing your partner using oral sex, the next chapter will explore various sexual positions to consider in order too enhance the sexual encounter.

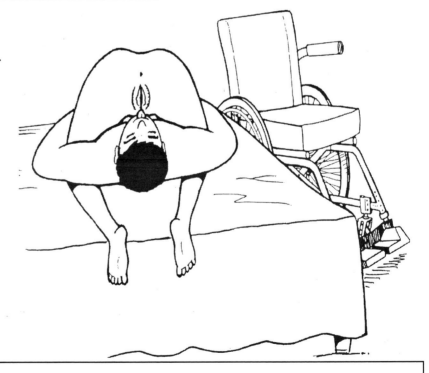

Figure 6.7 'Your shoulders outside of her legs and knees.' This position gives you more control and naturally exposes her vulva providing you with greater access.

Chapter 7
Sexual Positions

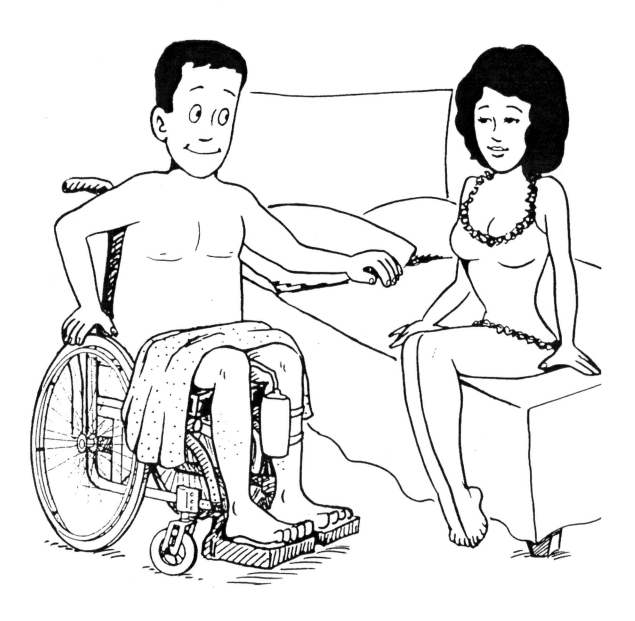

When we think of having sexual intercourse, most of us are familiar with the traditional missionary position. The typical picture that comes to mind when thinking about the missionary position is of a man on top of a woman laying on her back with her legs apart. This is a very difficult if not an impossible position for a paraplegic or a quadriplegic to perform successfully. Even if you are successful, your arms become very sore and tired as you attempt to hold yourself up. Intercourse should be enjoyable, not painful.

Sexual intercourse can be a pleasurable experience for both of you. It should not be avoided because of a spinal cord injury. In Chapter 4, I discussed techniques for obtaining an erection that will allow you to have vaginal penetration. Even though you may have limited feeling or no sensation at all in your penis, your partner will be able to experience sexual pleasure from having intercourse with you. If you have difficulty or are uncomfortable with this idea because of the extent of your paralysis, think of yourself as watching a live x-rated video, only you have the leading role. Just lie back and enjoy the show.

In this chapter we will show positions suitable for both paraplegic and quadriplegic males. The idea is to provide you and your partner with a number of options. Each position involves having access to different parts of the body and using different types of stimulation. Remember to openly communicate your desires to your partner. Discuss often what both of you want to do and what positions fulfill your needs the most. Centering yourself in your bed will give you the most room for movement and prevent you from falling out of bed. If you have leg spasms, tell your partner what she can do to help alleviate them. Discuss beforehand what position or positions you want to use. The positions discussed in this chapter will allow you and your partner to experience different pleasures while having intercourse. Several of them will allow for deep vaginal penetration, whereas others allow for shallow penetration. Some positions allow you to have access to your partner's breasts, clitoris or buttocks while having intercourse. A few will provide you with the opportunity to see your partner's vulva and your penis entering her vagina, which can increase your sexual excitement. Most of these positions are done in a bed. However, several, as you will see, can also be performed from your wheelchair.

A complication of a spinal cord injury is having limited body sensation. Therefore, it is important for you and your partner to be aware of how your body is reacting to the positions you are using. Always try to take precautions to prevent medical problems. For instance, avoid positions that could cause pressure sores. There shouldn't be a problem with your partner lying on top or sitting on top of you. You're not a china doll that's going to break if your partner puts her weight on you. Just make sure you are not having difficulty breathing while she is on top. If you do, tell her and try a different position. Once again the key to a good time is to openly communicate with each other. Also, avoid surfaces that can cut or tear the skin. Use surfaces that are cushioned and use various sized pillows to help position your body. I cannot emphasize enough that your physical comfort is important. Another precaution is to be aware of where your legs are positioned. If you have leg spasms, your legs can easily fall down over the side of the bed or become caught in the footboard, side rail, or in your wheelchair if that is where you are having sex. If something does not seem right and you start to sweat or your leg is twitching, stop what you are doing and check your body. Another issue of concern is bowel and/or bladder accidents (see chapter 3). Taking just a few simple precautions will help to ensure that you both will be able to enjoy your experience. Again, I remind you that having sex should be enjoyable, not painful.

Sexual Positions in the Wheelchair

Making love to your partner while in your wheelchair can be quite pleasurable and stimulating for both of you. Quadriplegics especially find that they feel the most secure and stable while in their wheelchair because maintaining their balance is easier with the seat belt and arms of the chair. Various sexual positions can be performed from a wheelchair. To begin with, your partner has the option of standing beside you or sitting on your lap. Other positions which can be performed from your wheelchair involve using a table, desk, or counter that you can wheel under and that will support the weight of your partner. Place some blankets and pillows on the table and have your partner lie back and get comfortable. She can comfortably rest her feet on your padded armrests or on your shoulders. This is a great position for oral sex, for using a sex toy, or for just exploring her vulva. The trick is be adventurous. Sex does not have to be performed only in a bed to be satisfying. Try the laundry room, the kitchen counter, or the workbench in the garage.

Wheelchair Position 1 - Sitting on your lap with your partner facing forward (away from you). This position is great for cuddling and kissing your partner's neck and ears (see Figure 7.1). You can also easily caress your partner's

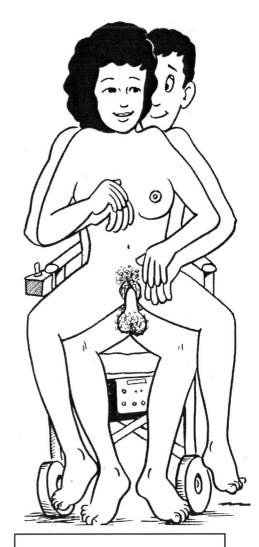

Figure 7.1 Wheelchair Position 1 Woman sitting facing forward.

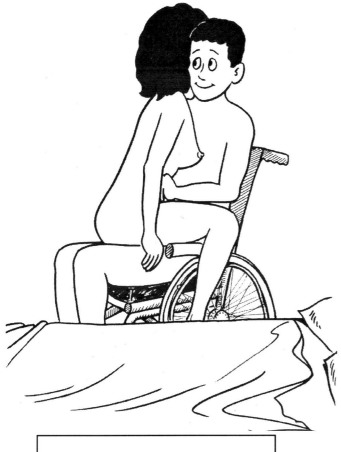

Figure 7.2 Wheelchair Position 2 Woman sitting facing towards you.

breasts in this position. In addition, you can easily reach around her to touch her vulva, directly stimulating her clitoris. It is possible to have vaginal intercourse from this position. Although, this may not be the best position for having intercourse, it is a great position for foreplay.

Wheelchair Position 2 - Sitting on your lap with your partner facing backwards (toward you). This position is more pleasurable if your partner sits on your lap placing her legs around the sides of the

61

wheelchair and wheels (see Figure 7.2). This is a good position for face-to-face contact and for talking, kissing, or just cuddling. This position allows you to easily caress her breasts, rub her back, or stroke her buttocks. It is possible to have intercourse from this position. For deeper penetration, however, move your hips forward on your cushion. This position will provide you with a good visual of your partner's vulva and your penis entering her vagina, which can be highly arousing.

Figure 7.3 The Woman-On-Top Position 1.

Sexual Positions in Bed

The Woman-On-Top. This position is preferred when the male partner has a spinal cord injury. It is the most comfortable and can produce various sexual experiences (see Figure 7.3). The woman can control the depth of penetration and what area of her vagina is being stimulated just by changing her body's position (see Figure 7.4).

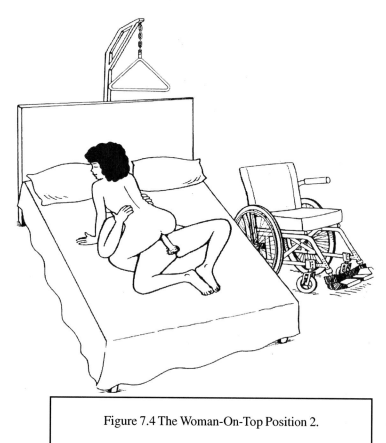

Figure 7.4 The Woman-On-Top Position 2.

This position (see Figure 7.5) can be very pleasing to you and your partner. In this position your penis stimulates the front wall of her vagina. This is also a great position for visual stimulation. Her vulva is wide open allowing you to see your penis enter the vagina. While your penis is inside your partner's vagina, she can assist you in going from a lying down position to a sitting position. This allows for a wonderful, intimate, face-to-face experience. You and your partner can have an intimate conversation, kiss, or just cuddle and enjoy the experience together.

A useful position for deep penetration involves moving your body to the corner edge of your bed (see Figure 7.6). Allow your feet to rest firmly on the floor to support your legs. Have your partner spread your legs and then lie back on the bed. Your partner will then straddle your legs while facing away from you. You can

Figure 7.5 Woman-On-Top Position 3.

do various things in this position. For instance, if you are able to maintain your balance, you can sit up and caress your partner's breasts. However, once you sit up, the depth of penetration becomes shallow. This position allows your partner to have maximum control of the depth of your penetration and rate and force of the thrust of your penis entering and exiting her vagina.

Personal Comfort

One area often neglected regarding sexuality is personal comfort. Although a couple can be creative and have a sexual encounter in various settings, most men with SCIs and their partners will have sex in a bed. Since the bed plays such a vital part in the sexual encounter, especially when one has a spinal cord injury, the following should be considered when choosing a bed to insure maximum comfort for you and partner: firmness, size, padding, age of your current mattress, and assistive equipment.

Firmness: A firm mattress will help you with transferring between the bed and the wheelchair; however, some individuals may find that a firm mattress causes pain and pressure on their hips, shoulders, legs, and feet. When purchasing a new mattress, insist on trying the mattress at the store to ensure that it will meet your needs and desired level of comfort. You should consider replacing your mattress if it is more than 10 years old, especially if it sags in the middle or is stained, soiled, or torn.

Bed Size: If you are considering purchasing a new bed, buy the biggest bed you can afford. "The bigger the bed, the better" is a good rule of thumb to follow. At the same time, remember to keep in mind the size of your bedroom and the need to allow for plenty of access so that you can freely move around the room in your wheelchair. Although you can have sex in any size of bed (e.g. twin, double,

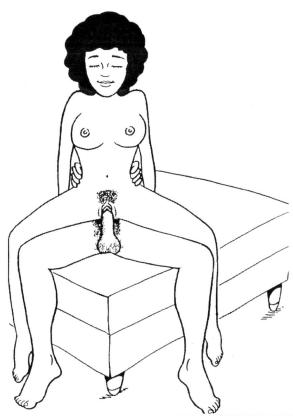

Figure 7.6 Woman-On-Top Position 4.

queen, king), a larger bed will give you and your partner more room to move and avoid feeling cramped. Larger beds also give you more opportunities to explore different sexual positions. Couples who have tried having sex in a single bed will tell you that it is very cramped particularly when one of the partners has a spinal cord injury. A double bed is better, but I would recommend a queen or a king. Because there is always the possibility of a bowel or bladder accident occurring in the bed you might consider purchasing a plastic fitted sheet in order to protect the mattress.

Padding: A major area of concern for individuals with a spinal cord injury is preventing pressure sores. During sex there can be times when your partner's weight could add undue pressure to those areas of your body that have contact with the bed. To help prevent pressure sores you could purchase a mattress with a pillow top or purchase an egg crate pad for the size of your bed. An egg crate pad can usually be purchased at any department store that sells bedding. The pad is put on top of the mattress, and then the bed sheets are placed on top of the pad. A second solution is to sleep on top of a sheepskin pad placed on the bed between your thighs and your shoulders. When these two pads are used together, they can be very effective in preventing pressure sores. The important issues to keep in mind are being comfortable and taking steps to prevent pressure sores. Experiment with different types of bed pads, sheets, comforters, and pillows to find what makes you the most comfortable. Having many pillows of various sizes and firmnesses can also be helpful. Pillows can be used to position and prop your body in various ways that are comfortable for you.

Assistive Equipment: A final consideration regarding the bed depends on your level of injury and the amount of usage in your arms. Do you need a trapeze, side rails, straps, or some other type of adaptive equipment to assist you in moving and repositioning your body while in bed? If you need such equipment, consult with a rehabilitation specialist or a local medical supply company that specializes in selling or renting medical equipment. What is important is to make yourself as independent as possible while in your bed so that you can be an active participant in a pleasurable sexual experience.

Setting the Mood and Making the Bedroom Sexy

Even though most couples have sex in the bedroom, they often neglect to consider making the bedroom a pleasant place to make love. Make your bedroom your little "love nest." It's very important that you and your partner are comfortable and secure in the room during your sexual encounter. Nothing is more embarrassing or kills the mood faster than interruptions, distractions, or someone barging into the room while you're having sex with your partner. Making your bedroom sexier helps to enhance the sexual encounter. The following are some ideas to consider.

Soundproofing: If you or your partner becomes vocal when sexually aroused or when having an orgasm, consider ways to soundproof the room, and I don't mean just put a sock in your partner's mouth. There is nothing wrong with moaning or being vocal when having sex. Ways of soundproofing the room would include using heavy carpet on the floor, hanging insulated curtains on the windows, hanging things on the walls, playing background music, or installing sound-insulation board over the walls and ceiling.

Lighting: Dim, indirect lighting is useful in setting a romantic atmosphere. Consider installing dimmer switches on overhead lights. Individuals who have ceiling fans with lights in their bedroom can purchase ones with remote controls that have dimmer switches that allow them to control both the brightness of the light and the speed of the fan. Strings of white lights such as those used on a Christmas tree can also be used. Rope lights are now the newest creation in lighting used for accent. They can be attached to or wrapped around almost any surface, cut to almost any length, and purchased in a variety of different colors.

Room Temperature: It is best if the room has its own temperature control, especially during the cold times of the year. For most people having sex in a cold room is not much fun. You can quickly raise the temperature of the room by using a space or ceramic heater. Some individuals have even installed a gas fireplace in their bedroom, which may not only heat up the room but may also help to set the stage and heat up the mood. Then all you need is a bottle of fine wine, two wine glasses, and some nice background music.

Mirrors: Some individuals like to watch themselves having sex. This can be especially true for men with spinal cord injuries because it allows them to visually experience more of the sexual encounter. When they cannot feel the physical aspects of sex, being able to see it happening helps them to experience a higher level of pleasure. Mirrors large or small can be used for this purpose. Larger mirrors can be installed on the wall or on the ceiling. If you want to be very creative in using mirrors in your room, for a maximum affect try placing the mirrors in a combination that will provide you with different viewing angles. As for smaller mirrors, a hand-held mirror can be used at any time to help the man see what is happening. Men often find it extremely exciting to watch their penis while it is in their partner's vagina. Men also enjoy watching their partner perform oral sex on them and can use the mirror to observe her in the process.

Room Décor: Everyone has different tastes when it comes to interior décor, and that includes decorating a "love nest." This is something you and your partner can plan together and have fun doing it. This would include the style of furniture, room colors, wall hangings, plants, lighting, and so on.

Music: Playing music can be rather helpful in setting the mood, but the choice of music should be one that you both can agree on. Usually soft rock, country, or new age music are some good choices for easy and romantic listening. Whatever your preference, be sure your partner also likes it. A poor choice of music can easily kill the mood. You don't want to play something that reminds you or your partner about someone else or about something unpleasant. An added benefit of music as I stated earlier is that it can be very useful in masking any sounds you and your partner make while having sex.

Door Locks: Make sure that you are able to lock the door of the bedroom, especially if there is someone else living in the house with you. There is nothing more embarrassing than someone such as kids, family members, or a college roommate barging into the bedroom while you and your partner are making love. In addition, if you have a service dog that knows how to open doors, make sure you remove the door opener or have a way to prevent the dog from opening the door should someone knock while you are indisposed. Trust me, this can be very embarrassing. It's the one time you will wish that your service dog had never learned how to open doors.

A Lockbox or Lockable Cabinet: Because most individuals with spinal cord injuries will use various erotic books, videos, DVDs, sex toys and pumps, it is important to keep your collection away from others. Find somewhere in the bedroom where you can keep your collection safe and secure.

Chapter 8
Enhancing Your Sexual Pleasure with the Use of Sexual Aids

Sexual aids, also known as sex toys, can greatly enhance your sexual experience. Sexual aids are especially useful for quadriplegics who have limited use of their hands and body movement. These aids allow you the opportunity to be in control of the pleasure you provide to your partner. Using a combination of the various sexual aids will provide you with the opportunity to please your partner time and time again. Regardless of your level of injury, the use of sexual aids can assist you in sexually pleasing your partner, and your partner can use them to please you. This chapter will explore the various types of sexual aids that are available. It will explain how sexual aids are used and which ones may be more suited to you and your partner's personal needs and pleasures. Before spending a lot of money on various sexual aids, you might take the time to discuss your options with your partner and make selecting sexual aids an enjoyable experience together.

Vibrators

The vibrator is usually the first thing people think of whenever they think of sex toys. Some individuals prefer to call a vibrator a personal massager. Regardless of what you call it, a vibrator provides continuous rhythmic stimulation to whatever area it touches. Did you ever go to a novelty gift store at the local mall and pass by the shelves that held the shiny silver, gold, and ivory vibrators and wonder who would buy them? Well, for a male with limited use of his hands and arms, a vibrator can be very useful in assisting him in satisfying his partner. A vibrator can provide her with constant stimulation which can bring her to a wonderfully pleasing orgasm.

Options in Choosing a Vibrator: Vibrators come in many different sizes ranging from mini vibrators, which are the size of a tube of lipstick and can easily be concealed in a purse or a backpack, to ones that are six to ten inches in length (see Photo 8.1 and Photo 8.2). Most vibrators are battery-operated; however, several plug into an electrical outlet. Vibrators come in a variety of colors including neons and pastels. Some are waterproof, so they can be taken into the shower or the bathtub. Vibrators also come in various textures, some are smooth, while others have dimples on their surfaces. Vibrators are made from various materials of which the most common is hard plastic, but more recently vibrators are being made of a soft jelly, which is very flexible. Also available is the new cyber skin vibrator, which feels just like real skin. Most vibrators are multi-speed and will allow the user to control the level of vibration. These controls range from a round knob on the bottom of the vibrator that can be turned to the desired speed to push button controls or slide controls which have preset speeds. There are also vibrators made specifically to stimulate the G-Spot.

Photo 8.1 Waterproof Mega-Mite™ with soft rubber oscillating tips.

Photo 8.2 Decadent Indulgence
A three point vibrator with 8 levels of accelerating vibrations.

Types of Vibrators:

One-Point Vibrators focus the stimulation in one area. These are the most commonly known vibrators (see Photo 8.3).

Two-Point Vibrators focus the stimulation in two areas at the same time. Some of these vibrators have a shaft that rotates and a vibrating clitoral stimulator. This vibrator stimulates both the vagina and the clitoris at the same time. The Beaver, the Rabbit and the Octo-Pussy are popular two-point vibrators (see Photo 8.4).

Three-Point Vibrators focus the stimulation in three areas at the same time. This class of vibrators is "the Cadillac" of the vibrator family. These vibrators are more expensive than the rest, but they are well worth the investment. They have a rotating and vibrating shaft, a clitoral stimulator, and rotating beads at the base of the shaft that stimulate the vaginal lips and kegel muscles of the vagina. The Jack Rabbit, Pearl Panther, and the Butterfly are three popular types (see Photo 8.5).

Guidelines for Choosing the Correct Vibrator:
Choosing a vibrator is a matter of personal preference. Discussing your preference with your partner is important. Choosing a vibrator together can be both fun and exciting, especially, when you and

Photo 8.3 One-Point Vibrators: Opulent Super-Slim.

Photo 8.4 Two-Point Vibrators: The Ultimate Beaver, Octo-Pussy

Photo 8.5 Three-Point Vibrators: Jack Rabbit, Pearl Panther, Pearl Butterfly.

your partner are looking forward to experimenting with your new toy. It is also wise to consider having more than one vibrator. A combination of vibrators can give you many more options, depending on your sexual desire. It is important to note that inserting hard plastic into your partner's vagina can cause pain and discomfort, particularly if it hits the pelvic bone or the bottom of the cervix. Therefore, it is better to use a soft jelly vibrator (see Photo 8.6) or a cyber skin vibrator (see Photo 8.7) if you plan to insert the vibrator into your partner's vagina or anus. Use the hard plastic vibrators for stimulating areas on the outside of the body. If you want to use a hard plastic vibrator internally there are various sleeves that can be placed over the vibrator making it safe and comfortable to use inside the vagina or anus.

Helpful Hint: If you have a hard plastic vibrator and intend to use a sleeve over it, place a condom over the vibrator before putting the sleeve on the vibrator. Heat produced when using the vibrator may make it difficult to remove the sleeve later. The condom will make it easier to remove it. Throw the condom away and clean the vibrator and the sleeve with mild soap and warm water after each use.

Warning: Do not use the same vibrator for both vaginal and anal use. Either use two different vibrators or use a condom on the vibrator when stimulating one area and then remove it in order to stimulate the other. This will protect your partner from infections.

Using a Vibrator: If this is your first time using a vibrator, try using it on yourself before involving your partner. Although it may seem awkward at first, allow yourself to relax and explore your body. Because the level of sensation varies with the level of injury, it is important to learn what you can feel and what feels good. Getting to know the sensitive areas of your body can assist you in communicating verbally to your partner what areas of your body have sensations and what feels good. You will be surprised at how a vibrator can help

Photo 8.6 Jelly Future Flex

you locate sensitive areas of your body that you never knew you had. It is also exciting and fun whenever you and your partner explore your body together. When using the vibrator, try different speeds and find the one that feels comfortable and brings the greatest pleasure to each of you.

Caution: Before using a new vibrator and after each use, be sure that it has been properly cleaned. This can be done by using a mild soap and warm water. Also, it is **never** a good idea to share your sex toys with someone other than your partner because of the possibility of HIV/AIDS and other sexually transmitted diseases.

When using a vibrator on a woman, it is not a good idea to go straight to the genitals. So, men, be forewarned (see Helpful Hints). Begin by stimulating other areas of her body such as her breasts, neck, back of her arms, or her thighs. Always pay attention to both your partner's verbal and non-verbal cues. Allow her to show you where the vibrator gives her the most pleasure. As you explore your partner's body, learn what areas of her body are sensitive. It is best to start using

Photo 8.7 Hygienically Superior Vibes

the vibrator at a low speed. Once again ask your partner what speed provides her with the most pleasure. Also, be considerate and warm the vibrator to at least room temperature before using it on her. Nothing can kill the mood faster than a cold vibrator if she prefers it warm.

Helpful Hints: The following are some suggestions for warming the vibrator in order to keep the passion flowing:

- Prior to use, hold the end of the vibrator under warm water (**do not use hot water**). If the vibrator is not waterproof, be sure that the controls and/or the battery compartment **do not** become wet.
- Consider using a heating pad to warm the vibrator. Place the vibrator on the heating pad, turn it on low, and then check the vibrator periodically to make sure it does not get too hot.
- Another option is to purchase a vibrator or a dong such as the Microwavable Hot Cock which can be warmed in the microwave prior to use. Be sure to read and follow the directions included with the product. Do not place a vibrator or dong in the microwave unless the directions state that it is safe to do so.

As you begin to explore your partner's genitals with the vibrator, begin by rubbing the vibrator over the top of the outer lips and the pubic area. The perineum, the area between the vagina and the anus, is a sensitive area that, when stimulated, can bring great pleasure. Allow the vibrator to slide in between the two outer lips in order to stimulate the clitoris. Listen to your partner to guide you and to determine how much direct stimulation to apply to her clitoris. If your partner is unable to tolerate the vibrator directly on her clitoris, try placing a towel or your finger between her clitoris and the vibrator. Do not rush. Relax and observe your partner's body reactions. Remember, you're not at the races where the first one to orgasm is the winner. Stimulating the clitoris too much too soon can be very painful to your partner. On the other hand, as she approaches orgasm, she may need more direct stimulation. Again, communicating with each other is very important.

Before inserting the vibrator into your partner's vagina, be sure the vagina is well lubricated. If there is not sufficient lubrication, inserting the vibrator can be painful. Usually a woman's vagina becomes naturally lubricated as she becomes sexually aroused. Extended foreplay can help with this process. Other options would be to use saliva or one of the many types of lubricating products made especially for this purpose (See **Lubricants** at the end of this chapter). Once the vibrator is properly lubricated, it can be inserted into the vagina. Once inserted, wait a few seconds to allow the vagina to adjust to the size of the vibrator. After the vagina has adjusted to the vibrator and has become accustomed to it, listen to what your partner wants you to do with it. Some women prefer to have the vibrator left inside the vagina without moving it. Others prefer the vibrator to be thrust in and out of the vagina simulating sexual intercourse. Still other women prefer a combination of the two. Listen to what your partner wants. In order for most women to have an orgasm from using a vibrator, the clitoris must be stimulated. The clitoris is the most sensitive area of a woman's genitals because of the high concentration of nerve endings within it. The vagina has very few nerve endings; therefore, stimulating just the vagina will not result in an orgasm. As always listen to your partner.

There are several high-tech vibrators available that come with a remote control. The Vibrating panty (see Photo 8.8) or the Remote Control Butterfly (see Photo 8.9) can add new excitement while doing "a night on the town." These items come with a vibrator either built into the panty or one that is strapped on which stimulates the clitoris. Your partner wears the panties and hands you the remote control. Having the remote control gives you total control of their pleasure. This can be an exciting form of foreplay and makes going shopping, out to eat, or watching a movie a fun adventure. Turning on the remote when she least expects it can be a lot of fun. It also helps you locate your partner should the two of you become separated and you need to find her. Just turn on the remote and listen for a response. The great thing about the whole situation is that you're having sex in public and no one knows it but you and your partner.

Dongs

A dong, also known as a dong, resembles an artificial penis. Most dongs do not vibrate, however, there are several specialty dongs that do. The main purpose of a dong is to penetrate the vagina. Dongs usually appear flesh-like with skin tones of ivory, brown, or black, but they also come in various colors (see Photo 8.10). They are usually made from latex rubber, but, there are some now made from a soft jelly material. Dongs usually range in length from 6 to 12 inches. They can vary in diameter from a 1 inch to a 2½-inch shaft (see Photo 8.11). The dongs also come in various textures making them easier to grip (see Photo 8.12).

Guidelines for Choosing a Dong: Choosing the correct dong can be a difficult decision, especially whenever you begin to look at all the different shapes and sizes offered. It is best for you to make the decision together. If the dong is too small, it will not be felt inside the vagina and will not provide much stimulation. On the other hand, if it is too large, it will be painful or uncomfortable. Men have a tendency to think big and therefore want to purchase the longest, widest dong offered. However, if it is uncomfortable for your partner, there is a good possibility that it will sit in its box instead of her. However, it is better to purchase one that is slightly larger than one that is too small. Just be sure it is not so large that it is unusable.

An inexpensive way to experiment with different sizes of dongs is to make one of your own. Fruits and vegetables make wonderful natural dongs. The most commonly used fruits and vegetables would include bananas, carrots, zucchini, and cucumbers. It can be quite erotic and exciting going to the grocery store with your

Photo 8.8 Remote Control Vibrating Panty

Photo 8.9 Remote Control Butterfly

Photo 8.10 Life-Like Dildos
Jumbo Jack Man-O-War

72

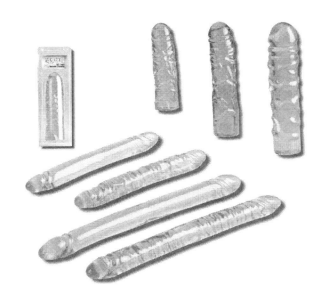

Photo 8.11 Translucent Soft Pink Jelly Dongs

partner to choose fruits and vegetables for this purpose. Only you and your partner will know what you'll be "cooking" later. Before using these items, be sure to clean them thoroughly with soap and water. Also, remove any rough edges or sharp areas from their surfaces before use. In addition, many household objects can also be used as dildos. Just look around and be creative. Whatever you decide to try just remember to clean it before and after you use it.

Using a Dong: Before inserting the dong into your partner's vagina, as with a vibrator, be sure that it is well lubricated. Even if your partner is extremely wet from her own natural fluids, it is still best to use additional lubrication on the dong. This will avoid any friction or damage to her vagina (see **Lubricants** at the end of this chapter). The additional lubrication will make penetration more comfortable and the experience more pleasurable. The larger the dong, the more lubrication you will need.

As mentioned above slowly insert the dong into your partner's vagina. Once it is inserted, wait a few seconds to allow the vagina to adjust to the size. Once her vagina has become accustomed to it, listen to what she wants you to do with it. Like the vibrators, some women prefer that the dildo be placed inside the vagina and left stationary while the man masturbates her or performs oral sex. Other women prefer that the dildo be thrust in and out of the vagina to bring pleasure. Some women prefer a combination of the two techniques. Ask your partner what she likes or prefers. Furthermore, let her be the judge of the depth of the insertion.

If you have good balance or are able to lean on your partner for support, it is possible to use a vibrator or a dong with one hand and to stimulate her breasts or other body parts with your other hand. Another area that is usually very sensitive on a woman is her anus. Inserting your finger into her anus as she nears her orgasm can be extremely pleasurable to her.

Warning: Never insert your finger or any object into your partner's anus and then insert it into her vagina. Inserting the same object into each opening can cause a serious bacterial infection.

If you are a high level quadriplegic with little or no use of your arms/hands, Swedish Erotica offers the Accommodator dildo. The Accommodator is a latex dong that fits on the chin and is held in place by straps

Photo 8.12 Super Jelly Dong

73

that go around the head. Once the dong is inserted into the vagina, you can use your mouth to stimulate her clitoris (see Photo 8.13).

Butt Plugs

Butt plugs are actually dildos made for the anus. A butt plug, however, is usually shorter and firmer than a dong. They are tapered on one end to ease insertion into the anus and wide at the other end to prevent it from becoming fully inserted or lost inside the anus. Butt plugs range in size from small to large. If you and your partner are interested in exploring anal sex, it is best to start with a small butt plug and work your way up in size (see Photo 8.14). When using a butt plug, always use plenty of lubrication. Never use a butt plug that has been used anally in a vagina. This could cause an infection or other medical problems. Always be sure to thoroughly clean your toys with soap and water after each use.

Warning: If you have little or no sensation in your anus, personal use of a butt plug is not recommended.

If you are a higher level quadriplegic, attempting to use a butt plug along with a vibrator or a dong can be more trouble than it is worth. If you find that you are spending too much time trying to hold everything in place and you're becoming tired, forget about the butt plug. It's not that important for pleasing your partner. The extra time spent trying to keep it in place can kill the romantic mood. If your partner prefers stimulation of her vagina and anus consider the Over & Under multi speed vibrator (see Photo 8.15). Discuss with your partner about her thoughts on anal stimulation. If she is uncomfortable with the subject, respect her opinion. Some women prefer "exit only" in this area.

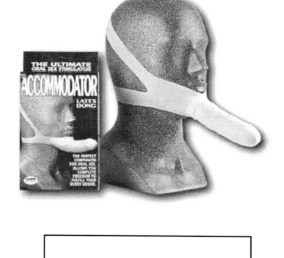

Photo 8.13 The Accommodator

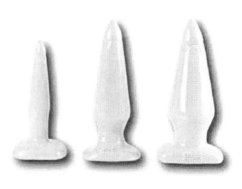

Photo 8.14 Back Door Probes

Photo 8.15 Over & Under Multi-Speed Vibrator

Eggs, Bullets, & Beads

Eggs, bullets, and beads are meant to be used by inserting them into either the vagina or the anus. The eggs and the bullets come with a built in vibrator that can be operated by an attached control unit (see Photo 8.16). There are several high-tech "eggs" and "bullets" available that are remote controlled. It can be rather exciting to insert the bullet or egg into your partner's vagina or anus and to tease them while you have total control of the remote and their pleasure (see Photo 8.17).

Warning: If you are going to insert a hard plastic egg or bullet into the vagina or anus, place it inside a condom. These items have been known to crack at the seam, or they can become stuck in the vagina or anus. If the unit should break during usage, the condom will keep the parts together and will make it easier to remove afterwards. The jelly eggs and bullets are safer to use because they are sealed.

Photo 8.16 Multi-Speed Egg

Beads can also bring great pleasure while having sex. They come in three sizes: small, medium, and large. They are also available in various colors. Like eggs and bullets, they can be inserted into the vagina or the anus. There is a string attached to them with a plastic ring at the end that you can slide your finger through to grip it if you are a quadriplegic with limited or no use of your hands (see Photo 8.18). The pleasure of using beads begins whenever you insert them into your partner's vagina. Be sure that your partner is wet enough before inserting the beads. If her vagina is not lubricated enough, use additional lubrication. Begin by inserting one bead at a time until they are all inside her vagina. If you have difficulty, ask your partner for assistance. Doing it together can add additional excitement and increase the pleasure for both of you. Once the beads are fully inserted, they can be left inside

Photo 8.17 Remote Control Egg

the vagina while you manually stimulate her clitoris or perform oral sex. The beads can also be pulled out at various speeds and angles creating different sensations. One of the most pleasurable times to pull the beads out of the vagina is during her orgasm. With practice you and your partner will learn what brings the greatest pleasure when using the beads. However you decide to experiment, have fun doing it!

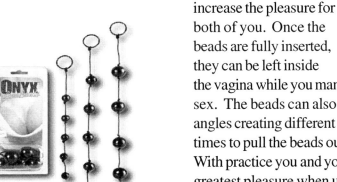

Photo 8.18 Onyx Love Beads

Warning: If you have little or no sensation at your anus, personal use of a bead, egg, or bullet is not recommended or should be used with extreme caution.

Another common product is the Ben Wa Balls. Ben Wa Balls are gold plated balls that are slightly larger than a marble. They are sold as a pair. Both balls are inserted into the vagina. As the balls move freely within the vagina, they can cause a high degree of sexual pleasure. The balls can be easily removed after your partner has her orgasm (see Photo 8.19).

Erection Rings

These are also known as cock rings, erection enhancers, or penile rings. This product is designed to help men have harder and longer erections. These rings are made to be placed at the base of the penis. As the penis becomes erect, the ring restricts the blood from leaving the penis which causes the penis to swell further and to become harder (see Warning below). These rings are made of metal, elastic bands, velcro leather, or

Photo 8.19 Gold "Orgasm" Balls

plastic. They range in size from small, medium, and large to one size fits all. Some rings come with a quick release; others are solid metal or plastic. Several have more than one ring, one that goes around the penis and one that goes around the scrotum. Some of the more popular types are the Lasso, Velcro Rings, and the Quick Release Erection Ring (see Photo 8.20).

Warning: Be extremely careful if you decide to use an erection ring. One of the main problems with using one of these and having a spinal cord injury is the lack of sensation in the penis. The other concern has to do with the amount of time the penis can be constricted. A ring can be on no longer than 20 to 30 minutes at which time it must be removed. If you are using a solid ring and are unable to get it off in time, it may have to be cut off with metal cutters or removed by medical personnel, which can be embarrassing and expensive.

Photo 8.20 Silver Erection Rings

Lubricants

As a woman becomes excited, her body naturally produces vaginal lubrication in preparation for sexual activity. However, there are times when a woman's body does not produce enough lubrication such as during times of stress, as a side effect of a medication, during certain phases of her menstrual cycle, following the birth of a child, as the result of a disability, or menopause. As a result, it may be helpful to use a commercially made lubricant which can be purchased at any local pharmacy or grocery store.

Types of Lubricants

Silicone Based Lubricants: Pharmaceutical-grade silicone lubricants are the longest lasting of all the lubricants and the slickest. Silicone can not be absorbed by the body, which is why it lasts longer than water or oil based lubricants. Most silicone lubricants are latex condom safe, but always remember to check the label. Since silicone is not absorbed by the body, it is flushed with your body's natural excretions. Pure silicone lubricants will not promote bacterial growth eliminating the risk of infections as a result of its use.

Water Based Lubricants: One of the best water-soluble lubricants known to individuals with a spinal cord injury is K-Y Jelly, which is used during bowel and bladder care. This lubricant is greaseless, will not stain, and is unscented. Water-soluble lubricants do not damage sex toys, nor do they break down the latex in condoms. This lubricant is easily removed from the body or sex toys with a mild soap and warm water.

Oil-Based Lubricants: These are not recommended for sexual use. Never use a petroleum-based lubricant such as Vaseline. Although oil-based lubricants are slippery, they are quickly absorbed into the skin. Bacteria can easily grow in oil-based lubricants which increases the chance for infection. Oil-based lubricants are not latex friendly and will break down latex condoms.

Erotic Videos, DVDs, & Games

A couple who is shy or needs a way to break the ice can do so by using erotic videos, DVD's, or various sexual games. These items can also be used to enhance or spice up a sexual relationship. Erotic videos can be used to set the mood, especially if one of the partners has difficulty getting started. Many individuals find that watching others having sex is a "sexual turn on." Watching erotic videos can also be educational, particularly if you or your partner have had limited or no sexual experience. A couple can learn various sexual techniques or positions by watching these videos in the privacy of their own home. It provides them with the opportunity to learn what turns each other on. Watching erotic videos can be used to explore their "wild side" or to fulfill each of their desires to participate in various sexual practices. The large selection of erotic videos available gives a couple the opportunity to view and explore various sexual activities such as oral sex, anal sex, or bondage. While I am unaware of any erotic video that features a male with a spinal cord injury as an actor, the movie "*Coming Home*" which can be rented at a video store, is about a Vietnam soldier that sustains an SCI during the war. This movie has a great sex scene. Even though an able-bodied actor is portraying a man with an SCI, the love scene is true to what a man with an SCI would do when having a sexual encounter with his partner. Another video dealing with SCI and sexuality which I would recommend is "*Sexuality Reborn*" produced by the Kessler Institute for Rehabilitation. This is an excellent video about SCI sexuality. It presents actual individuals with spinal cord injuries sharing their sexual experience.

Another option to consider is making your own personal erotic video. This can be fun and exciting. You can use various props, act out fantasies, and film your movies in different locations. Just remember to make sure that your video is kept in a secure place away from wandering eyes, especially those of children. Whatever you do, have fun and don't take it too seriously. If you do, it can kill the mood. It is also important that you both agree on when the video is to be viewed, by whom and what will happen to it if your relationship should end. This can prevent embarrassment in the future for you or your partner.

You and your partner can also help set the mood by purchasing sexually oriented games. An example of a sexually oriented game is Erotic Dice. This game includes a pair of glow-in-the-dark dice. One of the dice names body parts such as lips, leg, or breast; and the second one tells you what to do such as kiss, lick, or tease. Other popular sexual games include Fore-Playing Cards and The Loving Game. A creative couple can make up a game using a love mask, furry cuffs, a massage mitt, and other sexual toys. If making a mess is not a problem, try body finger paints or various flavors of body massage lotions on your partner. I'm sure there will be a flavor you and your partner will enjoy. If dressing sexy and role-playing sounds exciting try wearing some sexual attire. Sexual attire comes in latex, fishnet, and leather. These items include crotchless panties, teddies, thongs, catmasks, and fishnet gloves. Dress up as a nurse or a French maid and act out your favorite love scene or fantasy. Be creative, adventurous, and most of all have fun.

A Special Note: Each of the sexual aids mentioned in this chapter are products manufactured by California Exotic Novelties. These items, along with the games, lotions, and videos mentioned can be purchased through the author of this manual. Email the author at www.baernecessities.com and request a catalog of current available items and costs.

Chapter 9
Sexually Transmitted Diseases
Protect Yourself By
Knowing the Facts

Having a spinal cord injury does not protect you from contracting a sexually transmitted disease (STD), including HIV/AIDS, while having unprotected sex. There is only one way to be 100% protected from catching an STD - abstain from having sex. If you already have an STD, it is important that you let your partner know before you have sex with her so that precautions can be taken. If you become infected with an STD, it is very important that you **contact everyone** with whom you have had a sexual encounter.

STDs were once called venereal diseases or VDs. STDs are contracted by coming in contact with certain bodily fluids such as blood, semen, and vaginal fluids. When two individuals have sexual contact, these fluids can enter into the body through small micro tears in the skin of the penis, vagina, anus, or mouth. STDs can be passed during vaginal intercourse, oral sex, or anal sex.

There are more than twenty different types of STDs. This chapter will just briefly outline the main STDs by providing a brief description of the disease, how it is transmitted, the symptoms, and possible treatments. **The information presented in this chapter is for educational purposes only and should not be considered a substitute for actual medical advice or care. Therefore, if you think that you have been infected with an STD, seek medical treatment immediately.** A delay in treatment may be the difference between life and death.

As the recipient of a spinal cord injury, you have had to deal with one of the most traumatic experiences an individual could ever face during a lifetime. So you certainly don't need to add to your burden by incurring an STD. Take the time to read this chapter. Sex can be great, exciting, and wonderful, but it can also be deadly. Follow the safe sex suggestions given at the end of this chapter and sex can be everything you want it to be. Use the head on your shoulders before you use the one between your legs.

For further information about STDs and treatment consult your physician or contact the National Sexually Transmitted Disease Hotline at 1-800-227-8922 for general information and a listing of current support groups. Suggestions for additional reading regarding STDs, HIV/AIDS, and treatment are provided at the end of this chapter.

Vaginal Infections

Thrush: An infection caused by yeast.

Female Symptoms:
- An irritating itch and soreness of the vulva, vagina, and the perineum.
- Whitish, curdy discharge from the vagina.
- Skin around the genitals may become red and scaly and a rash may appear on the inner thighs.

Male Symptoms:
- A rash on the penis, scrotum, or the area around the genitals.

Treatment:
- Refrain from sexual intercourse until the infection is cured.
- Seek medical treatment.

Trichomoniasis: Commonly known as Trich or TV. The disease is primarily an infection of the vagina, but it can affect both men and women. In women the infection can also affect the cervix, the bladder, and the urethra, and in men it can affect the urethra and the prostate gland. Trich can be spread through sexual contact, shared towels and clothing, and toilet seats.

Female Symptoms:
- A painful burning sensation when urinating.
- Itchy, red and overall sore genitals.
- A smelly yellowish discharge from the vagina.

Male symptoms:
- Burning sensation when urinating.
- Discharge from the penis.

Treatment:
- Antibiotics such as Flagyl prescribed by a physician.

Bacterial Vaginosis:

Female Symptoms:
- A smelly discharge especially noticeable following sexual intercourse.

Male Symptoms:
- Men usually do not have symptoms. However, if your partner has been diagnosed with this infection, be sure that you are also treated.
- Possible redness or tender skin on the penis.

Treatment:
- Antibiotics such as Flagyl or Monistat prescribed by a physician.

Urethritis

Nonspecific Urethritis (NSU): This is one of the most commonly known STDs. The actual cause of NSU is unknown. When a person is infected with NSU, the symptoms will begin to appear within ten days following intercourse. It is also possible to catch NSU without having actual sexual contact. This STD mainly affects men. At some point the symptoms will disappear, and the infection will become dormant. However it is possible to spread the infection to others during this period of dormancy.

Female Symptoms:
- Women usually do not show symptoms of NSU.
- Some women will have vaginal discharge.

Male Symptoms:
- A tingling sensation at the tip of the penis.
- A clear fluid discharge from the penis, which becomes thicker if left untreated.

Treatment:
- Antibiotics

Chlamydia: The most common of the bacterial STDs in the United States. The cause for Chlamydia is the bacteria Chlamydia trachomatis, a microbial parasite that lives within the cells of the body. Chlamydia is spread through sexual contact including vaginal intercourse, oral sex, and anal sex. This is a very difficult STD to treat because the symptoms often go undetected. If left untreated, Chlamydia can cause serious health problems such as infertility.

Female symptoms:
- Usually no noticeable symptoms.
- Itching and burning of the genitals.
- Fluid discharge from the vagina.

Male symptoms:
- Painful urination.
- Clear watery or milky discharge from the penis.

Treatment:
- Antibiotics such as tetracycline prescribed by a physician.
- If left untreated it can result in infertility.

Gonorrhea: This is also known as the "clap." The cause of gonorrhea is a bacterium, Neisseria gonorrheae. Gonorrhea is spread through sexual contact including vaginal intercourse, oral sex, anal sex, and even kissing. If left untreated, gonorrhea can result in sterility and arthritis.

Female Symptoms: Usually none, but the following may occur in some women:
- Painful external genitals.
- Possible yellow discharge from the vagina or from the urethra.
- A painful burning sensation while urinating.
- Abnormal menstrual bleeding.

Male Symptoms:
- A yellowish discharge from the penis.
- Sores around the genitals.
- A painful burning sensation while urinating.

Treatment:
- Antibiotics such as ditton, ceftriaxone or doxycycline prescribed by a physician.
- No sexual contact until 100% cured.

Genital Ulcers

Genital Herpes: A viral infection which can be caused by two different types of viruses: herpes simplex 1 or herpes simplex 2. Herpes affects both men and women alike. Although there can be symptoms or signs of having herpes, they do not always manifest themselves. Therefore, you may not be aware that you have been infected.

Herpes is highly contagious, particularly during times of a visible outbreak. An outbreak can be activated by stress, illness, or the menstrual cycle. When a herpes infection is not active, it is said to be dormant. It is

82

during these times when spreading of the disease to a partner is less likely but not impossible.

Symptoms for both males and females:
- Facial cold sores, usually around the mouth.
- Tender genitals that are sore to the touch.
- Painful, fluid-filled blisters on the mouth, throat, or genitals.
- Flu-like symptoms such as headaches, fever, and vomiting.

Treatment:
- There is no known cure for herpes at this time. Once you have contracted herpes, the virus remains in your body for the rest of your life.
- There are medications such as Acyclovir which can relieve some of the symptoms and shorten the outbreak.
- Use of stress reduction and relaxation techniques can help to control the symptoms.

Syphilis

This infection (also called "pox") is caused by a spirochete, a very tiny microorganism. Syphilis is spread through sexual contact including vaginal intercourse, oral sex, and anal sex. One can also be infected with syphilis by sharing infected drug needles, receiving tainted blood during a transfusion, or a mother can pass it to her newborn child during the birth process. Syphilis in most cases can be cured; however, if left untreated, it is fatal. The symptoms of syphilis progress through a series of three stages.

First Stage - Appears three weeks following contact with the spirochete.
- Chancre, which look like open sores or ulcers, first form on the genitals wherever the infection comes in contact with the skin. These chancre look like hardened red pimples on the penis, vulva, or vagina. Within two to six weeks the chancres will disappear, even without treatment.

Second Stage - Begins after the chancres have healed, which can be anywhere from one week to six months.
- A rash on the hands and other parts of the body.
- Fever.
- Sore Throat.
- Swollen glands.

Third Stage - May appear ten to twenty years after being infected.
- Heart Disease.
- Blindness.
- Paralysis.
- Brain Damage.
- Death.

Treatment:
- A blood test is the most common medical procedure for diagnosing syphilis.
- Antibiotics such as penicillin or tetracycline are commonly used to treat syphilis during the first and

second stages.
- Both partners need to be treated at the same time to prevent them from re-infecting each other.

Genital Warts

Symptoms:
- Small cauliflower like bumps on the genitals.

Treatment:
- There is no known cure for genital warts. Once they are removed from the genitals, it is possible that they will grow back.
- Genital warts can be removed by liquid nitrogen, lasers, surgery, or podophyllin liquid. Warts left untreated can become cancerous.

Crabs (Pubic Lice)

Crabs are one of the easiest STDs to spread and the least serious. They can be transmitted through bodily contact, shared towels or bed sheets, or an infested toilet seat. It is possible to see these tiny bloodsucking creatures with the naked eye. Crabs tend to cause severe itching of the genitals, but they can also migrate to other parts of the body such as the head or eyelashes. If you suspect that you are infected with crabs, check your underwear for possible tiny blood spots. The treatment for crabs involves Kwell or Malathion, which can be purchased at your local pharmacy. In addition, using a fine-tooth comb in your pubic hair can help rid yourself of the eggs. You should also consider shaving your pubic hair, which can provide some quick relief and speed up the treatment process. You will have to wash all of your underwear, bedding, towels and clothing in hot water to kill the unwanted guests. Finally, you should alert your partner and any house mates so that they can be checked and treated if infected.

Scabies

Scabies is another type of microorganism that can be transmitted during sexual contact or by sharing towels or bed sheets. Scabies can live anywhere on the body. They cause severe itching. The treatment is the same as with crabs, applying Kwell. However, the Kwell must be applied to the entire body and left on for 24 hours before it is rinsed off. A second treatment should be applied ten days later to kill any of the eggs that have hatched. Anything with which you have come in contact must be cleaned including clothing and bedding. Anyone with whom you have had physical contact, either sexually or casually, needs to be warned and treated. Scabies are difficult to get rid of because they can spread very quickly.

Hepatitis

There are several types of hepatitis. The most common forms are A, B and C. There are over 5 million people in the U.S. currently infected with some form of Hepatitus. Hepatitus is a virus that is usually spread from one person to another in specific ways for each form of the virus. Hepatitus A is spread through contact with fecal matter, unsanitary food, contaminated water, or shellfish. Hepatitus B and C are spread through contact with infected blood, sharing IV drug needles, tattooing and body piercing, and sharing personal care items (toothbrush, nail clippers, razors, and nail files). Hepatitus B is also spread through sexual contact. Unlike B, the risk of contracting Hepatitus C through sexual contact is extremely low. Hepatitus C is the most serious form of Hepatitus and should be treated as soon as possible. If left untreated Hepatitus C can cause serious liver damage leading to liver failure. For more information about Hepatitus C contact your physician.

Symptoms for A and B:

During the early stages:
- Fever.
- Headache.
- Rash.
- Aching joints.
- Loss of appetite.

During the later stages:
- Jaundice (a yellowish tint to the eyes and skin).
- Chalky stool.
- Dark urine.

Treatment:
- Bed rest.
- A vaccination specifically developed for hepatitis.

HIV & AIDS

AIDS (**Acquired Immune Deficiency Syndrome**) is a deadly incurable virus. The virus that causes AIDS is known as **HIV** (**Human Immunodeficiency Virus**). It is believed that the AIDS virus originated in the rural communities of Africa. The virus spread as those who had contracted the virus moved from the rural areas into the larger populated cities and became sexually active with others or gave blood for transfusions. AIDS was first detected in the United States in the early 1980s. At first AIDS was thought to affect only the homosexual community; however, the number of new cases reported among the heterosexuals has significantly increased each year. We now know that anyone who is sexually active can get AIDS no matter what his/her sexual orientation may be.

HIV/AIDS is transferred through semen, vaginal fluid, and blood. The virus can be transferred during vaginal intercourse, oral sex, or anal sex. In a heterosexual relationship a man can pass the virus to his female partner through his semen while a woman can pass the virus to her male partner through her vaginal fluid.

It is not possible to become infected with AIDS through casual contact with someone who has the virus. Giving someone a hug or shaking the hand of someone with AIDS will not transfer the virus. AIDS cannot be contracted by kissing someone with the virus unless open cuts or sores are present on the mouth or lips. AIDS is not normally transferred through saliva. In order to contract AIDS through the saliva of an infected person, you would have to drink a gallon of their saliva; and even then your chances of becoming infected with the virus are still very minimal. It is also not possible to contract AIDS as the result of an insect bite such as from a mosquito, or a bee that has bitten or stung someone with the disease.

Individuals who are at high risk of contracting AIDS are those who practice unsafe sex, have multiple sexual partners, and/or are intervenous drug users who share needles. In addition, women who are pregnant and infected with AIDS/HIV have a chance of passing the virus to their unborn child.

It is very important that you take precautions to protect yourself especially if you fall into one of the risk groups. If you are sexually active protecting yourself begins by practicing safe sex. When the virus first enters the body, it begins attacking the white blood cells known as T-cells. This produces a weakening of the immune system; as a result, the body is unable to defend itself against germs and infections. When someone is first infected with HIV, there is a considerable drop in the T-cell count. As the virus multiplies, it tricks the body into thinking that it is a T-cell. It does this by genetically altering its structure to resemble T-cells, but in reality the virus is reproducing itself. Then the virus goes into a state of hibernation which can last for several years. This is why people carrying HIV are often unaware that they are infected with it. They don't exhibit any symptoms. In the meantime, if they continue to be sexually active or share needles with others (drug users), they are spreading the virus. At some point the virus, which has been dormant, explodes like a time bomb and attacks, in overwhelming numbers, the body's few remaining healthy T-cells. The immune system becomes extremely weak and the individual is now diagnosed with AIDS. Those who have AIDS usually do not die from the virus itself but from some type of infection such as the flu. Because of a weakened immune system, the body cannot fight infections that healthy immune systems can. Therefore, it is very important that you take precautions to protect yourself, especially if you are a member of one of the high risk groups. If you are sexually active, protecting yourself begins with practicing safe sex.

Guidelines for Safer Sex

- Always use a condom with a new partner or one whose sexual history is unknown (See "A Word about Condoms" below).
- If you or your partner have open sores, cracked skin, or are bleeding, be extremely careful. These conditions increase the risk of becoming infected with STDs.
- Do not share your sex toys with others.
- Be sure your sex toys are properly cleaned following each use. If they are not, they can carry infections.
- Never share a hypodermic needle with anyone for any reason.
- If you are performing oral sex on a new partner or on someone whose sexual history you know very little about or nothing at all, take some precautions. STDs including AIDS can be spread through oral-genital contact. Until you truly know your partner, oral sex can be performed in ways that make it safer for both partners. For example a flavored condom can be placed over the penis. A piece of latex, dental dam, or a condom that has been cut in half can be placed over the vagina while performing oral sex on a woman.
- The fewer sexual partners you and your partner have had the lower the risk of either of you becoming infected with an STD.
- The more sexually active you are with multiple partners the greater your risk for contracting STDs.
- Maintaining personal hygiene is very important. Always wash your genitals daily and wear clean underwear. If you do not wear underwear (which many individuals with SCIs do not), be sure your clothing is clean and dry, especially around the genitals.
- If you wear an external catheter, be sure your genitals are cleaned daily. The catheter can hold moisture and create added heat, which makes an excellent breeding ground for bacteria.

A Word about Condoms

A condom is a sheath that is worn over the penis during sexual intercourse to prevent a sex partner from becoming pregnant or for protection against most STDs. Condoms can be easily purchased over the counter at a drug store or grocery store. They are convenient because you do not need a doctor's prescription to purchase them. You may be telling yourself that using a condom is a moot point because you have a spinal cord injury. It is true that the risk of your partner becoming pregnant is low, but the risk of you becoming infected by most STDs including HIV still remains high. If you are going to be sexually active, using a condom is the only way of protecting yourself from most STDs. It is recommended that you use a condom if you answer "yes" to any one of the following situations:

- This is your first time with your partner, and you know very little about her sexual history.
- You or your partner have had unprotected sex with multiple partners.
- You or your partner use IV drugs and share needles.
- You or you partner have a known STD or HIV/AIDS.

For the highest level of protection against most STDs and HIV while using a condom, it is recommended that you use latex condoms lubricated with Nonoxynol 9. It has been proven that Nonoxynol 9 destroys HIV and the AIDS virus and is therefore a greater form of protection from HIV and AIDS than a condom alone. Avoid using lambskin condoms. These condoms have small openings (pores) that allow various STDs, and HIV to pass through the condom. When using a latex condom, avoid using oil based lubrications such as baby oil, vaseline, or hand lotions. Oil based lubrications tend to break down the latex reducing the amount of protection. For individuals who are allergic to latex there is the polyurethane (plastic) condom. It offers the same amount of protection as does the latex condom. The polyurethane condoms have several advantages over the latex condoms. They are stronger, can be used with any type of lubrication, and offer more sensitivity to the male using them. Condoms are also available in various flavors. These condoms are used mainly during oral sex as a protection from STDs.

If you are a quadriplegic and/or have limited use of your hands, you may find it difficult if not impossible to put on a condom. **Do not** avoid using a condom or talk yourself out of using a condom just because you cannot physically put one on yourself. You need to be able to ask your partner to put the condom on your penis. If your partner has already gone through the process of transferring you from your wheelchair to the bed, undressing you, and removing your catheter and leg bag, putting a condom on your penis is just one more step in the process. Putting on a condom is the same as putting an external catheter on the penis. If you are still uncomfortable with your partner helping you, discuss this before you get into bed. Explain your concerns or apprehensions. The best thing to do is to incorporate putting on the condom into foreplay. This can reduce your feelings of embarrassment, and it is foreplay because it involves direct manual stimulation of your penis from your partner. Furthermore, if your penis has any open sores such as blisters caused by the friction from wearing an external catheter or there is cracked, dry skin on the penis from the use of a skin prep or alcohol swabs, or if you and your partner are **not** in a monogamous relationship, use a condom to prevent infections. If you have an indwelling catheter, the tip of the catheter can be bent back towards the penis. Then the condom can be unrolled over both the catheter and the penis. If you have an indwelling catheter and are sexually active, speak to you neurologist or family doctor for their recommendations about using condoms. The one thing to always keep in mind when using a condom is that it is best to follow the manufacturer's directions.

The basic steps for using a condom.

1. Always use a new condom and be sure that it is undamaged before using it.
2. Check the expiration date on the package. If the date has expired, do not use it. The condom may become dry and develop cracks with age reducing the amount of protection.
3. It is easier to put the condom on if the penis is erect.
4. Pinch the tip of the condom as it is placed on the head of the penis to release any trapped air.
5. Unroll the condom down the shaft of the penis toward its base and the pubic hair. While doing this, try to squeeze out any air that may become trapped between the condom and the penis. This will ensure a secure fit, increase sensitivity, and prevent the condom from breaking.
6. Be sure the condom is on properly before the penis comes in contact with your partner's genitals.
7. If you have an ejaculation while having intercourse, grip the condom at the base of the penis as you remove your penis from the vagina to prevent the condom from coming off and to prevent the semen from spilling out. Remove the condom from the penis and throw it in the trash.
8. After sexual intercourse it is always a good habit to wash your genitals in order to prevent infections and to maintain proper personal hygiene.

The Don'ts of using a condom:

- **Don't** try to reuse a condom.
- **Don't** use an expired condom.
- **Don't** allow the penis to have contact with the vagina prior to putting on the condom.
- **Don't** use oil based lubricants unless it is a polyurethane condom.
- **Don't** substitute a male external catheter for a condom.
- **Don't** use a condom if there is a hole in its packaging.

Suggested Readings and Resources

Jussim, D. (1997). <u>AIDS & HIV: Risky Business</u>. New Jersey: Enslow Publisher, Inc.

Marr, L. (1998). <u>Sexually Transmitted Diseases: A Physician Tells You What You Need to Know</u>. Baltimore: The John s Hopkins University Press.

Moglis, R. F., & Knowles, J. (1997). <u>All About Sex: A Family Resource on Sex and Sexuality</u>. New York: Three Rivers Press.

Chapter 10
...And Their Adventure
Continues...

In writing this manual there were two main goals that I wanted to accomplish. First, I wanted to assist men with SCIs and their partners to become aware of their sexuality. Having a spinal cord injury does not brand you a non-sexual, undesirable human being who is incapable of loving or of being loved. We need to rid our society of those myths and stereotypes about sexuality and having a disability. We can do this by becoming involved in life and showing others by our actions that individuals with SCIs can have "normal" relationships with other individuals. What matters most is that you are able to look past your injury and your limitations and focus on your strengths and on being yourself. If you like who you are and believe in yourself others will feel comfortable around you and want to be with you. Secondly, I wanted to explore different ways of being sexually active with your partner. Regardless of your level of injury, it is possible for you and your partner to have a "normal" sexual relationship. However, this may mean having to redefine how you and your partner express yourselves sexually. The use of various sexual positions, oral sex, and various sexual aids can all help you and your partner have a satisfying sexual relationship. Remember to practice safe sex especially if the relationship is new. Enjoy what you are doing but be safe in doing it.

For couples seriously wanting to have children, I have shown you that there are several options. It is possible to have an SCI and father a child, and it is possible for you to be a good parent. As the medical advancements in the area of SCI fertility continue, the number of men with SCI successfully fathering children will continue to increase.

Appendix A
Product Listing and Information

The following is a listing of the companies and their products that were mentioned throughout this manual. You can purchase or obtain further information about these items by contacting the company and requesting to speak with a sales representative. The sexual aids mentioned throughout this manual including the lotions, games, and videos can be purchased through the author of this manual. To receive a listing of items and item recommendations, please contact the author at: www.baernecessities.com.

Product Listing

California Exotic Novelties, Inc.
14235 Ramona Ave.
Chino, CA 91710
www.calexotics.com
Items: Vibrators, dildos, butt plugs, penis pumps, and various other sex toys.

Endocare, Inc.
6585 City West Parkway
Eden Prairie, MN 55344
Phone: 800-863-3445
Items: StayErec™ Syetem, Dura-II™, ErectAid®System

Orion Medical Group, Inc.
9272 Jeronimo Rd. 119
Irvine CA 92618
Phone: 949-598-8415
Item: FERTI CARE® personal

U.S.A. Jeans
9744 E. 55ᵗʰ Place
Tulsa, Ok 74146
Phone: 800-935-5170
www.USAJeans.net
Items: Wheelchair jeans and slacks

Books about sexuality and spinal cord injuries:

Title: *Accent on Living*

Reprint Series, Number 1
This book includes three articles:
- "The Disabled Person and Family Dynamics"
- "Sexuality and the Disabled Female"
- "Sex and the Spinal Cord Injured Male"

Accent on Living magazine
Box 700
Bloomington, IL 61702
309-378-2961

Title: *Sexual Adjustment: A Guide for Spinal Cord Injured*
By: Martha Ferguson Gregory
Note: This book can be purchased through Accent on living magazine.

Title: *New Horizons in Sexuality After a Spinal Cord Injury*
By: Pamela J. Bielunis, MHS, PTII
Note: This book can be purchased through Accent on living magazine.

Title: *Sexuality After Spinal Cord Injury: Answers to Your Questions*
By: Stanley H. Ducharme & Kathleen M. Gill
Note: This book is published through the Paul H Brookes Publishing Company.

Video about Sexuality and Spinal Cord Injuries

Title: *Sexuality Reborn*
Note: This video can be purchased through the Kessler Institute for Rehabilitation, West Orange, New Jersey. The video is approximately 45 minutes in length.

Title: *Coming Home*
Note: The video can be rented at any local video store.

Appendix B
Review Questionnaire

Review Questionnaire

Name: _____

Profession: _____

This manual, "Is Fred Dead? A Manual On Sexuality For Men With Spinal Cord Injuries," was designed to be informative, assist with sexuality adjustment, and improve relationship satisfaction. To ensure that this manual meets your expectations, please take a few minutes to complete this questionnaire and return it. Your opinions are extremely important to me and will provide me with valuable feedback regarding your satisfaction. Thank you for your valued assistance

1. What is your overall impression of this manual in regard to the usefulness of the information presented? Using a scale from 1 to 5, where 1 is not helpful at all and 5 is very helpful, how would you rate this manual? 1 2 3 4 5 (Please Circle One)

2. What did you find most useful about the manual?

_____

_____

3. Do you feel the organization, layout, pictures, drawings, explanations, and candor of the manual is appropriate and helpful?

_____

_____

4. What changes would you recommend?

_____

5. In the space below or on another piece of paper, please write any additional comments or suggestions for improving this manual.

_____

_____

Thank you for purchasing this manual. Should you have any questions or suggestions that you would like to Email to me, send them to dr_hayyou@hotmail.com.

References

Anderson, C. J. (1997). Psychosocial and sexuality issues in pediatric spinal cord injury. *Topics in Spinal Cord Injury Rehabilitation, 3*(2), 70-78.

Auerbach, S. M. (1983). Impotence and the inflatable penile prosthesis. *Paraplegia News,* August, 27.

Bensman, A., & Kottke, F. J. (1966). Induced emission of sperm utilizing electrical stimulation of the seminal vesicles and vas deferens. *Archives of Physical Medicine & Rehabilitation*, 436-443.

Berger, F. G. (1988). *The G-Spot in Words and Pictures*, Flensburg: Orion.

Bielunis, P. (1995). *New Horizons in Sexuality after a Spinal Cord Injury*, Bloomington, IL: Accent Press.

Brackett, N. L., Padron, O. F., & Lynne, C. M. (1997). Semen quality of spinal cord injured men is better when obtained by vibratory stimulation versus electroejaculation. *The Journal of Urology*, 157, 151-157.

Buchanan, L. E., & Nawoczenski, D. A. (1987). *"Spinal Cord Injury" Concepts and Management Approaches*, Baltimore: Williams & Wilkins.

Cole, T. M. (1975). Sexuality and physical disabilities. *Archives of Sexual Behavior*, 4(4), 389-403.

Cole, T. M., & Glass, D. D. (1977). Sexuality and physical disabilities. *Archives of Physical Medicine & Rehabilitation,* 58, 585-586.

Derry, F. A., Dinsmore, W. W., Fraser, M., Gardner, B. P., Glass, C. A., Maytom, M. C., & Smith, M. D. (1998). Efficacy and safety of oral sildenafil (viagra) in men with erectile dysfunction caused by a spinal cord injury. *Neurology*, 51, 1629-1633.

Ducharme, S. H., & Gill, K. M. (1997). *Sexuality After Spinal Cord Injury: Answers to Your Questions*, Baltimore: Brookes Publishing Co.

Ellis, R. G. (1980). The corona-frenulum trigger, A specific stimulatory technique of reflexively triggering the ejaculatory and orgasmic response in spinal cord injured males. *Sexuality and Disability*, 3(1), 50-56.

Gregory, M. F. (1974). *Sexual Adjustment: A Guide for the Spinal Cord Injured*, Illinois:Cheever Publishing, Inc.

Guldin, A. (2000). Self-claiming sexuality: mobility impaired people and american culture. *Sexuality and Disability*, 18(4), 233-238.

Higgins, G. E. (1979). Sexual response in spinal cord injured adults: A Review of the Literature. *Archives of Sexual Behavior*, 3(2), 173-196.

Hirsch, I. H., Seager, S. W. J., Sendor, J., King, L., & Staas, W. E. (1990). Electroejaculatory stimulation of a quadriplegic man resulting in pregnancy. *Archives of Physical Medicine & Rehabilitation, 71*. 54-57.

Hohmann, G. W. (1972). Sex and the spinal cord injured male. In *Accent on Living Reprint Series, 1,* Bloomington, IL: Accent Press.

Johnson, D. L. (1993). Grieving is the pits. In Singer G. H.S., & Powers, L. E. (ed.) *Families, Disabilities, and Empowerment: Active Coping Skills and Strategies for Family Interventions,* (pp. 151-154), Baltimore: Paul H. Brookes Publishing Company.

Jussim, D. (1997). *AIDS & HIV: Risky Business,* New Jersey: Enslow Publisher, Inc.

Leyson, J. F. (1990). Ejaculatory dysfunction. In J. F. Leyson (Eds) *Sexual Rehabilitation of the Spinal Cord-Injured Patient,* New Jersey: The Humana Press, Inc.

Linsenmeyer, T. A. (2000). Sexual function and infertility following spinal cord injury. *Physical Medicine and Rehabilitation Clinics of North America,* 11(1), 141-156.

Linsenmeyer, T. A. (1991). Infertility in men with spinal cord injury. *Archives of Physical Medicine & Rehabilitation,* 72, 747-754.

Linsenmeyer, T. A. (1991). Evaluation and treatment of erectile dysfunction following spinal cord injury: A Review. *The Journal of the American Paraplegia Society,* 14, 43-51.

Linton, S. S. (1990). Sexual satisfaction in males following spinal cord injury as a function of locus of control. *Rehabilitation Psychology,* 35(1), 19-27.

Lizza, E. F. (1990). Infertility evaluation and management after spinal-cord injuries. In J. F. Leyson (Eds) *Sexual Rehabilitation of the Spinal Cord-Injured Patient,* New Jersey: The Humana Press, Inc.

Master, W. H., Johnson, V. E., & Kolodny, R. C. (1995). *Human Sexuality,* New York: Longman.

Marks, J. L., & Light, J. K. (1990). Surgical treatment of impotence. In J. F. Leyson (Eds) *Sexual Rehabilitation of the Spinal Cord Injured Patient,* (pp 265-277), New Jersey: The Human Press, Inc.

Marr, L. (1998). *Sexually Transmitted Diseases: A Physician Tells You What You Need to Know,* Baltimore: The John s Hopkins University Press.

Maytom, M. C., Derry, F. A., Glass, C. A., Smith, M. D., Orr, M., & Osterloh, I, H. (1999). A two-part pilot study of sildenafil (vViagra™) in men with erectile dysfunction caused by spinal cord injury. *Spinal Cord,* 37, 110-116.

Miriam, S. (1991). *The Magic of Sex,* New York: DK Publishing Inc.

Milligan, M. S., & Neufeldt. (1998). Postinjury marriage to men with spinal cord injuries: Women's perspectives on making a commitment. *Sexuality and Disabilities*, 16(2), 117-132.

Moglis, R. F., & Knowles, J. (1997). *All About Sex: A Family Resource on Sex and Sexuality*, New York: Three Rivers Press.

National Spinal Cord Injury Statical Center, (2000). *Facts and Figures at a Glance*, Birmingham University: Alabama.

Nehra, A., Werner, M. A., Bastuba, M., Title, C., & Oates, R. D. (1996). Vibratory stimulation and rectal probe electroejaculation as therapy for patients with spinal cord injury: Semen parameters and pregnancy rates. *The Journal of Urology*, 155, 554-559.

Nemeth, S. A. (2000). Society, sexuality, and disabled/ablebodied romantic relationships. In D. O. Braithwaite & T. L. Thompson (Eds.), *Handbook of Communication and People with Disabilities Research and Applications,* (pp 37-48). New Jersey: Lawrence Erlbaum Associates Publishers.

Ohl, D. A., Menge, A. C., & SØNKSEN, J. (1998). *Penile Vibratory Stimulation in SCI Males: Optimized Vibration Parameter and Process Factors,* Ann Arbor, Michigan.

Perkash, I. (1986). Fertility: A challenge in spinal cord injured patients. *Paraplegia News*, 28-30.

Rieve, J. E. (1989). Sexuality and the adult with acquired physical disability. *Nursing Clinics of North America*, 24(1), 265-276.

Rutkowski, S. B., Geraghty, T. J., Hagen, D. L., Bowers, D. M., Craven, M., & Middleton, J. W. (1999). A comprehensive approach to the management of male infertility following spinal cord injury. *Spinal Cord*, 37, 508-514.

Scheutzow, M. H., & Bockenek, W. L. (Spring 2000). An unusual complication during electroejaculation in an individual with tetraplegia. *The Journal of Spinal Cord Medicine*, 23, 28-30.

Seeley, R. R., Stephens, T. D., & Tate, P. (2000). *Anatomy & Physiology*, (5th Ed) New York: McGraw Hill.

Sipski, M. L. (1991). Spinal cord injury: What is the effect on sexual response? *The Journal of the American Paraplegia Society*, 14(14), 40-43.

Sipski, M. L. (1996). Sex after spinal cord injury. In *Spinal Cord Injury Manual*, (pp 1-25), New Jersey: Kessler Institution for Rehabilitation.

Senelick, R. C., & Dougherty, K. (1998). *The Spinal Cord Injury Handbook for Patients and Their Families*, Birmingham, Alabama: HealthSouth Press.

Sporer, G. (1990). Male sexuality. In J. F. Leyson (Eds) *Sexual Rehabilitation of the Spinal Cord Injured Patient* (pp 39-53). New Jersey: The Humana Press, Inc.

Stanway, A. (1998). *A Couple's Guide to Loving: Frank, Accessible, Expert Advice for Lovers*, New York: Carroll & Graf Publisher, Inc.

Stanway, A. (1989). *The Art of Sensual Loving: A New Approach to Sexual Relationships*, New York: Carroll & Graf Publishers, Inc.

Stanway, A. (1992). *The Lovers; Guide: the art of better lovemaking*, New York: St. Martin's Press.

Trieschmann, R. B. (1990). Sexual harmony despite impotence. In J. F. Leyson (Eds) *Sexual Rehabilitation of the Spinal Cord Injured Patient*, (pp 39-53), New Jersey: The Humana Press, Inc.

Vogel, L. C., Klaas S. J., Lubicky, J. P., & Anderson, C.J. (1998). Long-term outcomes and life satisfaction of adults who had pediatric spinal cord injuries. *Archives of Physical Medicine and Rehabilitation*, 79, 1496 -1503.

Zejdlik, C. P. (1992). *Management of Spinal Cord Injuries*, (2), Boston: Jones & Barlett Publishers, Inc.